G000168135

Fanny Frewen was born in ..... away from home to beco..... Aircraft Site. After the war ..... and then worked on *Vani*..... before making her career in advertising where she wrote, among others, the first eighteen Oxo commercials. She now lives in Kent with her husband, Stephen, and writes full time. *The Sunlight on the Garden* is her second novel.

Praise for *The Tortoise Shell*

'*The Tortoise Shell* has the texture and flavour of the lovingly distilled, whose prose has been allowed onto the page only after a proper gestation . . . Sharp as a knife and yet deeply compassionate, Fanny Frewen is an original spirit'
The Times

'Funny, wise and totally captivating'
Lynda Lee-Potter

'A romp of a read, full of high jinks and quirky insight'
Mavis Nicholson

'A joy to read'
Publishing News

ALSO BY FANNY FREWEN

The Tortoise Shell

The Sunlight on the Garden

Fanny Frewen

ARROW

Published by Arrow Books in 1997

1 3 5 7 9 10 8 6 4 2

Copyright © Fanny Frewen 1997

Fanny Frewen has asserted her right under the Copyright,
Designs and Patents Act, 1988, to be identified as the author
of this work

This book is sold subject to the condition that it shall not,
by way of trade or otherwise, be lent, resold, hired out, or
otherwise circulated without the publisher's prior consent in
any form of binding or cover other than that in which it is
published and without a similar condition including this
condition being imposed on the subsequent purchaser

First published in 1997 in the United Kingdom
by Century Books

Arrow Books Limited
20 Vauxhall Bridge Road, London SW1V 2SA

Random House Australia (Pty) Limited
20 Alfred Street, Milsons Point, Sydney
New South Wales 2061, Australia

Random House New Zealand Limited
18 Poland Road, Glenfield
Auckland 10, New Zealand

Random House South Africa (Pty) Limited
Endulini, 5a Jubilee Road, Parktown 2193, South Africa

Random House UK Limited Reg. No. 954009

A CIP catalogue record for this book
is available from the British Library

Papers used by Random House UK Limited
are natural, recyclable products made from wood grown in
sustainable forests. The manufacturing processes conform to
the environmental regulations of the country of origin

ISBN 0 09 964961 6

Typeset by SX Composing DTP, Rayleigh, Essex
Printed and bound in Great Britain by
Cox & Wyman Ltd, Reading, Berkshire

To James Hale
guide, philosopher and friend

The sunlight on the garden
Hardens and grows cold,
We cannot cage the minute
Within its nets of gold,
When all is told
We cannot beg for pardon

The Sunlight On The Garden
Louis MacNeice
1907–1963

I

It was a natural thing for Laura and John Fenby to give their Anniversary Party at the Beaters' Arms. The one they'd given for their Silver Wedding had been Swanmere's great night out. So it was more than hinted at that a smaller do, now that the Fenbys had been married for thirty years, would be a great way to bring in the month of April. Worth dieting off winter's fat for.

The party started at five o'clock. Five o'clock was the right time. It suited everybody in Swanmere.

'Will I do? Do I look all right?' Laura asked her husband at 4.45. She always thought she liked the idea of a party but what she really liked was planning it far enough ahead that something might, by some fortunate chance, cause it not to happen. Even at fifty-three, she had not learned about inexorability. As usual, she put off dressing until the last minute.

'You look very nice,' said John. Unable to say aloud that she looked adorable, he poured a glass of champagne and gave it to her as she sat at her dressing table. He had recognised, all day long, the symptoms of her nervousness, such as moving things out of their places and back again, trying to arrange the flowers that had been sent, and tidying the bookshelves by the expedient of taking the books out and piling them on the floor.

Laura drank her champagne. She preferred humbler wines but she knew what John meant, so she turned her face up and kissed him.

She had got into her pale green silk blouse, dark green velvet waistcoat and dark green velvet long skirt. John liked her in it, and it had the added advantage of being comfortable, and not too tight. New for the occasion was the necklace of silver set with pale green peridots, John's gift. She put it on without looking in the mirror.

That Laura's hair was almost white was lost on John. He had married an ash-blonde girl, nine years his junior, and she was still an ash-blonde girl to him. He loved her and he bossed her about. He would not have described himself as 'Master of the house'; indeed describing himself at all was quite outside John Fenby's ways. He had just, on marriage, automatically taken up that position, as had his father before him and his grandfather before that. Entirely without conceit, it never occurred to him to think other than that he knew what was best for his wife and family. It was a system that worked well for Laura who, the only child of an unhappy marriage, was delighted to love and be loved by her husband. Most of the time she went her own sweet way, in any case.

The Fenbys had two sons and two daughters. Peter was twenty-nine, Judy twenty-eight, Ann twenty-seven and Luke twenty. Judy and Ann had been born within the same year, Judy in January and Ann in December. 'Are you sure, Mrs Fenby,' asked an official over some form she, as mother, had to fill out, 'that you haven't made a mistake?'

'Not sure at all,' Laura had said, 'but not the mistake you're thinking of.' Someone, she couldn't remember who, had told her that it was impossible to conceive within two months of a birth. Hrrmph!

Luke had come as a bit of a surprise. After the arrival of such a rapid houseful, Laura and John's love-making had been perpetually interrupted by the rattle of little hands on the bedroom doorknob, and cries of 'Mummy, I want a drink of water.' However, one by one, the older three children eventually started in school and so, fortunately, the girls in particular, much as they loved their mother, developed a fine contempt for her intellect. When Judy came home able to count up to one hundred, Laura suggested she continue. 'Oh, Mummy, don't be silly. There aren't numbers after a hundred.'

'There are, darling.'

'No. Not at school. There are a hundred. And that is that.'

Peter, Judy and Ann got puppies and kittens that Laura had to feed and rescue from dehydration. But at last she was free at night to make uninterrupted love with her husband. This had led to a careless moment, and resulted in the arrival of Luke.

'Have you got a comb in your handbag?' John asked Laura now. She hastily put one in, beside the cigarettes she tried not to smoke.

Entering the Beaters' Arms, Laura was thankful that they had not taken the car. John, like a dog getting its basket into order, would always park and re-park the car at least three times before he was satisfied. 'You go on in, don't get cold,' he would say, and Laura would have to go into wherever it was, by herself, which she hated.

Whenever there was a party in Swanmere, especially one as desirable as this, the party of the year, people got there bang on time. John and Laura walked in, arm in arm, to the upstairs room, reserved for such occasions, to a welcoming buzz. Someone called out, 'Here comes the bride and groom,' followed by a few voices humming 'Pom pomtipom, pompomti*pom*.'

Laura looked with amazement at the spread of food. John had taken the whole business of the food out of her hands. 'Nope,' he had said, 'not this time.' Laura had taken a lot of trouble to learn to cook. John had never cooked a meal in his life, and never did so now, even though he was at home for two or three days in the week. The solicitor's practice in the county town, twenty miles off, of which he was the senior partner, could well, he had decided, do without his permanent presence. 'We don't, goodness knows,' he had said to Laura, 'go in for high drama with our clients.'

John had been cheerfully unaware that his midday presence not only deprived Laura of a privacy she had come to value, but also let her in for cooking yet another meal. So she was very touched that now he had arranged all this. Well, he had got caterers and the help of Betty, the landlord's wife, but it was the thought that counted.

Gradually, faces became recognisable. 'Lovely, this,' said Mrs Bean. Laura was fond of Mrs Bean, who no longer needed to go out cleaning but wouldn't desert Mrs Fenby. It was Mrs Bean's view (correctly held) that Mrs Fenby couldn't manage without her. Laura bought household equipment entirely under instruction from Mrs Bean. Mrs Bean informed her that her trash-bucket was unhygienic, and made her buy a swing-lid bin that was fine as long as you didn't put anything in it. Laura left the lid off; Mrs Bean put it back on.

They had been intimates through childbirth, illnesses and the mixture of love and hatred induced by ageing parents. Mrs Bean's father had had a stroke, and been difficult with it, just at the same time as Laura's mother, Veronica Chadwick, had discovered sex, but not with Laura's father. Mrs Chadwick's window-cleaner, though taken by surprise, had been more than willing to oblige, in the spare room, and the gardener found there was a whole new meaning to rose-pruning. He, however, was overcome by guilt about poor, nice Colonel Chadwick, and gave notice, leaving Mrs Chadwick to complain that you couldn't rely on anyone, these days. Then there was Mrs Bean's prolapse and Mrs Fenby's bout of pneumonia. But they still addressed each other as 'Mrs'.

Mrs Bean was holding a plate of prawns and rice. 'This makes a nice change,' she said. Mr Bean was taking the ham, with salad. 'You look really nice,' Mrs Bean continued.

'Do I? Do you really think so?'

'You look like a girl.'

Laura knew she looked like no such thing, but accepted the compliment and strove to reciprocate. 'You look jolly nice, too. You look like a queen,' she said, with truth. Mrs Bean did look exactly like the Queen. And she was having such a good time that Laura decided that now was not the moment to break the latest news to her. In fact, Laura wished, for the moment, to put it out of her own mind. For her mother, Mrs Chadwick, was about to move in on the Fenby household, her long-suffering husband, Laura's father, having quite suddenly turned up his toes, and gone to his reward while reaching for a bound volume of *Punch*.

Luckily, she was distracted by the arrival of Marion and Jeremy Clark. The Clarks lived in a house called Swanmere Cottage. It belied its name of cottage, being much bigger and very much smarter than the Grange, where Laura and John lived.

She liked Marion Clark, even though Marion was perennially thin. Laura was by no means fat, but four babies had extended her perimeters somewhat, and any feeble attempts at dieting were always curtailed by John's liking her as she was. For some reason, John was slightly disapproving of Marion's husband, though he couldn't say why. Marion was about thirty-eight and Jeremy, who could tell? The crisp, curling hair, black going on grey, was hard to put an age to. The Clarks had no children. Jeremy commuted to London.

The friendship between Laura Fenby and Marion Clark had started as Swanmere friendships always did. It was the custom for older wives to take the lead over younger wives, especially if newly arrived. Some were kinder than others, and Laura was squarely in that category. And, having so rapidly filled cradle after cradle herself, Laura had naturally assumed that Marion would soon be doing the same. Secretly sentimental, she was a non-thrower-away and it would have been a pleasure to find a home for the big pram, the cot, the climbing frame and the pushchair.

But now nearly twenty years had gone by, with no babies

in the Clark household. When John Fenby said, after the first year or so, 'Funny those two haven't started a family. Why haven't they?' Laura made no reply. For all that she had become really fond of Marion, she regarded that kind of questioning as impertinent and unkind, especially from someone as productive as herself.

Swanmere gradually stopped staring at Marion's unchangingly slim waistline. Mrs Bean gave Laura her opinion that it was a pity but sometimes you couldn't help envying Mrs Clark, and Swanmere society availed itself of her dinner parties. The Clarks' dinner parties were grand affairs, with freshly ironed linen napkins, and elegant crystal, all in full, unbroken sets. Laura had long gone over to seersucker napkins, and hadn't had a set of matching glasses since the children had learned to pour out their own Cokes.

This evening, Marion was wearing an outfit that had clearly cost a lot of money. Laura had never seen it before but that wasn't surprising. Jeremy, who had become popular in Swanmere, was wearing a suit that sat well on him, and an old school tie.

'Marion, how nice!' said Laura. 'Thank you for the lovely bowl.' The wedding anniversary gift from Marion and Jeremy Clark had been delivered a day ago. They would never turn up with a last-minute purchase of flowers to be left withering among the coats. Marion and Jeremy always did things right.

John kissed Marion, a little awkwardly. This was partly because he had never quite got the hang of this business of everyone kissing women who were not their mothers, wives or daughters, and partly because he was never quite sure what one should talk about to women who hadn't got children, unless of course they were spinsters, in which case gardens or dogs were the theme. He shook Jeremy's hand, and asked 'How's the City?' He always asked Jeremy how the City was, as though the City were a sick relation, and Jeremy always answered, 'Good,' or 'A bit slow at the moment.'

'We've only just got here,' said Marion. 'I've seen Peter and Judy but not Ann and Luke.'

'You've seen more than I have, then,' said Laura.

'Hallo, Ma,' said Luke, appearing noisily.

'Luke, darling, how nice. I'm glad you could get here.'

'Only just. I say, Ma, you couldn't spare me some money, could you? I've just MOT'd the car –' he put on a virtuous expression to go with this proof of responsible behaviour – 'and see, it, like, needs a few things done.'

'We'll see. Go and say hallo to Daddy. You might even congratulate him. And me.' Laura didn't have favourites, or so she said.

'Oh, right. Brill. Got it.' He disappeared for a moment and returned looking even more virtuous. 'I brought you flowers.' He held out a hideous bunch, obviously bought at the last-stop garage forecourt. A few chrysanthemums; Laura wondered where garages got chrysanthemums from at this time of year; one clashing lily and some of those everlasting things Laura was glad she could never remember the name of. As Laura moved on, flowers in hand, he turned to her friend.

'Hallo, Marion. Give us a kiss.'

'Forward boy,' said Marion, enveloped and liking it. 'Who's that?' she asked, pointing to the girl with Luke's elder brother.

'That? Oh, that's old Pete's new bird. Looks a bitch, doesn't she?'

'Don't let your mother hear you say that.'

'Oh, I know. Poor old Ma, she's always full of hope instead of sense, when it comes to Pete's girls. I say, your glass is empty. Let me fill it.'

'And yours, I presume, you brat.'

'Of course. I've left the car at the house, so don't worry.' Luke took interest in his welfare for granted. Marion knew that, like his mother, he found it easy to like people, as a result of which he cheerfully thought it perfectly natural that they should like him. He was only ever censorious about the

7

girlfriends of his big brother. In fact, from trotting adoringly, at one year old, behind his then ten-year-old brother, he had somehow come to adopt, as the years went by, the 'uncle' role.

Easter was only just past. Easter Sunday, a week ago, had begun, and continued, with icy rain and lowering clouds. Dorothy Carew, wife of Theodor Carew, Swanmere's vicar, had said, on meeting Laura in the churchyard, 'Christ is risen.' Her daughter and only child, Jennifer, was twenty-three, but a late-comer, hence Mrs Carew's adherence to old forms. 'So He has,' replied Laura, hoping the paschal lamb in her oven wasn't spoiling while privately thinking that, on a day like this, He would have been better advised to remain in the tomb.

But on this glorious evening of the Fenby party, the sun shone and everyone was having a wonderful time. John was circulating benevolently, returning whenever possible to Theodor Carew. He liked Theodor, who managed to walk the tightrope between understanding the ways of the young and not mucking up the old form of service. John was on the Vestry Committee, and he took the plate round on Sundays.

Jennifer Carew was being edged away from Peter by the girl Luke had described as a bitch. She – her name was Deirdre – wasn't that bad. In fact, she was quite pretty, dark and bosomy. She looked, Laura thought, a little tight-lipped. But then, after all, Peter had plunged her straight into the middle of a family party, where she knew no one. It was so typical of Peter, just to telephone at the last minute and mutter that he'd like to bring someone with him. All Laura had been able to elicit was that it was a girl whose name was Deirdre.

Laura had never been quite at ease with her first-born. He had come so soon. He cried a lot and she had difficulty in doing the decent thing for him with breasts that had so recently been the sole prerogative of her husband. She had never mentioned this to John, who was charmed with the son she had provided. But, an only child herself, she knew nothing about babies, and she had always felt guilty about inflicting her maternal apprenticeship upon Peter.

She had found her little girls much easier. She would take Peter on her lap, while she was feeding Judy. 'Did you do that for me, Mummy?' he asked.

'Of course I did.'

'I don't remember.'

She wondered if Peter's bringing this girl to what was very much a family party signified anything. He had been out with a few girls but, so far, shown no signs of wanting to marry. Her main hope was that he should marry someone really loving. She also, although she told herself that her opinion didn't matter, very much wanted to like whoever it might be. So, if this was to be the one, she *would* like her.

She had been looking out of the window at the setting sun. But here was Betty, landlady and wife of the landlord of the Beaters' Arms, asking had everything been all right.

'Perfect, and thank you so much.'

'Glad you're pleased.'

'Laura, it was a lovely party,' said Marion. 'But we must go. I've got the builders coming in, first thing tomorrow.'

'Oh Marion, poor you. How awful. I can't stand having builders in the house. What are they going to do?'

'The new bathroom.'

'Oh, of course.' Marion had been poring over brochures and colour charts for weeks on end, Laura reminded herself.

The Clarks were about to have a third bathroom. The Fenbys' one bathroom ought at least to have been done up a bit. But that would have meant the awful business of throwing out the old plastic ducks and Luke's purple-dog sponge, not to mention the magazines long stuck by damp to the cork-topped stool. 'It'll be lovely, when it's done,' said Laura. 'I envy you.'

Jeremy kissed Laura. John kissed Marion. Luke bounded up and kissed Marion and said to Jeremy, 'Lucky old you, going home with the prettiest girl in the room.'

9

'He's a live wire,' said Betty. Her husband was hoping they were nearly through, but he was a good-natured chap. Betty had worked hard to help Mr Fenby to make a success of the evening, and if she wanted to settle in now and have a good time, so be it. Betty watched, fascinated, as Luke kissed Jennifer Carew, who clearly enjoyed it but had better not hope for anything serious, not with that Luke. What a naughty boy!

She didn't much like the look of Peter's young lady. A husband-hunter, in her opinion. Oh well, none of her business.

'You've done wonders tonight, Betty,' said John Fenby. 'Time you had a drink. What can I get you?'

'A small port, thank you.'

'A small port it is, then. Not too small, if you don't mind. I'll join you,' said John.

Judy Fenby watched her brother Peter. She knew that he and she were thought to be alike, in being the two quiet ones, where Ann and Luke were the ebullient ones. That resemblance was true, but there it ended. Peter was not ambitious. Her mother, she observed, was being nice to Deirdre. Judy, who was always cautious, reserved her judgement.

Suddenly, there was a loud explosion of sound. The Beaters' Arms prided itself on being one of the last decent pubs in existence, and so didn't have music. But they had reckoned without Luke, who had gone out to his car and collected his portable stereo.

The noise was deafening. To John Fenby, however, one lot of music was very much like another, and was for dancing to. He led his wife on to the floor and executed a foxtrot with a dash of old-fashioned waltz.

'John,' said Laura, 'you're stroking my bottom!'

'And why not? What are wives' bottoms for, if not to be stroked, I'd like to know?'

Mr Bean gave up on the white wine, to him no better than lemonade, and got into the beer. It was after midnight before Mrs Bean got him home.

2

Marion Clark was up early, dressed and spreading dust-sheets through the hallway, up the staircase to the landing, and also through the bedroom doors, for good measure.

Jeremy, who had no need to ask for a clean shirt, since his shirts always hung in rows, ironed and in order, called out, as he tripped over a dust-sheet, 'Is breakfast ready?' a redundant question, as he knew very well that his muesli and wholemeal toast would be put before him as it always was, just as his briefcase was always waiting for him by the front door. He was always given poached eggs, grilled bacon and buttered toast on Sunday, the day when cricket in summer, or village football in winter, worked them off.

Jeremy left his house to go to the City. He went into the kitchen to kiss his wife goodbye. She was scrubbing some saucepans. 'I thought you'd just bought new ones. Aren't those the ones you are going to throw out?'

'Yes, but,' said Marion, knowing what she was doing was ridiculous, but continuing to do it just the same.

The builders arrived no more than an hour late, instantly managing to track the dirt off their trainers through the kitchen, the one place Marion had missed with the dust-sheets. The head builder, Mr Bagshot, although Marion had been through her brochures and colour charts with him at least three times, had in the back of the van a load of tiles in shades of Weetabix. There was a bit of a tussle about this. Mr Bagshot had got the tiles free, from the last job, and now said to Mrs Clark 'I can do you a nice price, on these.'

Mrs Clark said 'No.' Mr Bagshot expressed surprise. At last, knowing a hard woman when he saw one, he gave in and solaced himself by spreading tools, thermos (in case Mrs Clark was too mean to make them coffee) and one of those radios that can play two stations at once, with tin-tack accompaniment, on the upstairs landing.

The most junior builder, bearing a pail of something grey and sloppy, wandered into the drawing room. 'I must not,' said Marion to herself, 'lose my temper. I want this bathroom. I have wanted it for months.' With all the restraint she could muster, she led the lad out of the drawing room and up the stairs.

Marion hated disorder but was seldom faced with it. She had been a naturally tidy child and, having married young, had gone straight from her own neat bedroom to her own neat home. Bypassing the years when most girls shared flats, she had no idea what it was like to share a bathroom with other people's semi-clean washing, or a living room with three-day coffee mugs on the carpet, and dubious items under the sofa.

Now, with heroic restraint, she recognised that the only thing to do was to walk away. So she went into the garden.

The first part of the garden was very like the inside of the house. A paved patio was neatly surrounded by reproduction urns, awaiting the garden-centre purchases that filled them every spring. Then came a neat lawn. Then came a strange place.

The neat lawn gave way to a slope, which in turn led to a small jungle. Jeremy Clark, forbidden by his wife to raise a finger in the house, prided himself on his gardening. He mowed the lawn in stripes. His Access card was favourite at the garden centre, where he could be relied upon to buy up every chancy shrub, from plumbago to *Japonica kewensis*, at great expense.

Marion walked until she could no longer hear the builders'

radios, until she found herself in her wild garden.

It was not a warm day. Not cold, just April-ish. She had never thought about who had owned Swanmere Cottage before Jeremy had bought it. She had never discussed the private place below the proper garden. Rhododendrons ran riot over it. The apple trees had gone crab, and the wild roses mingled with long-unpruned but still scented roses, dark reds, pale-veined whites and apricot yellows, their names unknown to her.

Laura's children had loved to play here, when they were little. But as they were the only people, other than Marion, who penetrated this wilderness, the strange contrast between it and the impeccable interior of the house had never been commented upon. Even Marion herself did not quite know why she had never wanted it landscaped, or even tidied. She had told herself she left it like that because it was so much enjoyed, as it was, by her friend's children. A swing still hung from the branch of a cedar tree. But, though the children were all grown up, the garden was just as wild as it had ever been.

If, in the house, Marion had so much as pulled a thread in the cloth of her skirt, or laddered her tights, she would not have been able to bear another moment without changing. In this wild garden, the brambles pulled at her hair, rough goosegrass wound itself through her legs, and her shoes were immediately soaked through, as she pushed her way into its very heart. Her only carefulness was to look down and make sure she was not treading on the little spring flowers which she knew would be pushing their way up.

She was as familiar with every bit of ragged, wilful growth, in here, as she was with every neatly folded item indoors. She saw nothing strange in that, it was just a different sort of order. A small silver birch had fallen and lay, paper-light, on the ground, home to all sorts of insects, any one of which would have been hustled out of the house in a dustpan. She picked up a beetle that had fallen on its back, and set it gently on its feet, for which kindness it nipped her finger. She said 'You rotter,' and licked her finger.

The faithful cherry tree was coming into flower. It was a white cherry, and looking up through it at the now-blue sky was so beautiful an experience it quite simply took her breath away. She sat on the ground, and closed her eyes.

She could hear, in memory, the children's voices now. Judy, bossily to Ann, 'You'll get your frock dirty,' and Ann's happy reply, 'Don't care, it's tore anyway.' And Luke, up the tree, 'I've gone too high, gemmy down.' When Peter used the swing, he used it solemnly and silently. Mostly, he liked to touch things. He said he liked their feel. He had been an odd, gangly little boy, with none of Luke's easy demonstrativeness. Luke cuddled anyone within reach. Peter might shyly put out a finger and touch Marion's face, and then dart away. He was found to be short-sighted and, by the time he was seven, needed to wear glasses.

Deprived of her usual morning activity, which was fussing and polishing, Marion allowed her wild garden to lull her into doing nothing but think. Her wretched failure to give Jeremy children, especially a son, came over her as she got up and idly pushed the disused swing back and forth. She never wept about her barrenness when she was busy in the house. But here, among the primroses and the first bluebells, and with no one to see her, she gave way to the relief of a few tears.

She remembered the first time she had noticed Jeremy, or, rather the day that he had noticed her. It was the day her mother died.

'I am afraid,' her father had told her, 'that your dear mother is no longer with us.' Marion, aged eleven, hadn't understood what he meant, and was so embarrassed by this announcement from the gentleman she had always had to address as 'Father' not 'Daddy', that she burst into silly laughter.

'Do you not understand me?' Ralph Carpenter knew nothing about girls. His wife had provided him only with this daughter, a creature totally perplexing to a man whose life was dedicated to his profession of schoolmaster, and now housemaster, in a minor public school for boys only.

Apart from the begetting of his one child, an act which of course succeeded holy matrimony, Mr Carpenter knew very little about females. Even if the child had been a boy, his acquaintance with it would only have taken place with its clothes on. Although he was far from unkind, changing nappies and bathing babies would have been none of his business. His now late wife, poor soul, had just died of cirrhosis of the liver, having used the bottle as a substitute for passion. He was quite unaware of this. Laetitia had always worn Pringle twin-sets, jerseys and cardigans with ladylike but unflattering necklines, in shades of beige, sage, pale blue and dusty pink.

No more words were exchanged, between father and daughter. Marion was puzzled. Mr Carpenter stood, fingering a book on his desk, as the child, silent and apparently unmoved, walked out of his study.

The schoolboys, who knew that Mrs C. had snuffed it, fell back as the little girl passed through them, along the dank stone passageway with its rows of smelly boot-holes, and out into the garden.

Jeremy Clark was the handsomest boy in the school. He had absolutely no homosexual leanings and was big enough and tough enough to frighten the daylights out of anyone, older or younger than himself, who tried it on. And with his prefectorial privileges, he had no problem in getting out for a nice time on Saturday nights. It was an easy bicycle ride into the nearby town, where a jolly time always awaited him, with a very agreeable lady pharmacist, whose husband worked away from home a lot and who knew, with the whole contents of a chemist's shop available to her, how to take care.

He found skinny little Marion, her head against a wall, white-faced, and looking as though she was about to be sick. 'Hallo, little one,' he said, recognising his housemaster's daughter. 'What's the trouble?'

'I don't know. I think my father is annoyed with me.'

'Oh, come. He's upset, because your mummy has died. That's all.'

'Oh,' said Marion. 'Is that what's happened?'

Jeremy, simply thinking 'Poor little brute,' put his arms round her, not realising that such an easy gesture on his part was to affect the rest of his life. In the eleven years of *her* life, Marion had had very little experience of being cuddled. Her mother, though kind enough in her own vague way, had not been a lap-mummy. And her nanny, who had also been her mother's nanny, was rather more of the 'It's bedtime, say your prayers and don't forget God bless –' the list would follow – 'and brush your teeth properly' school than the 'kiss-goodnight and hug-me-tight' persuasion.

So when Jeremy, a man of eighteen years old, took, just for kindness, skinny little Marion Carpenter into his brawny arms, her die was cast. As was his.

Jeremy wanted no truck with university. What he wanted was to get to the City as soon as possible, and start making money.

While he was doing this, Marion was growing up in total ignorance of the life of other girls. For Ralph Carpenter, a meticulous educator of boys, simply did not believe in schooling for girls. She was allowed to attend French classes, but not Latin or Greek. And certainly not biology! The music master gave her some piano lessons, but she had no aptitude. She avoided the kitchen, where the grubby old cook, who came cheap, slopped out vats of greasy stew and the repulsive suet-and-sultana puddings that the boys called 'sore legs'. Marion would have liked to help the housekeeper and the maids, but the last thing they wanted was Sir's daughter hanging about and listening. So she was forced back into her own little bedroom, which she cleaned and tidied as meticulously as her father taught boys.

Having no contact with other girls, and only with the boys *en masse*, when they couldn't avoid her entirely, she went through adolescence in complete ignorance of giggles, secret telephone conversations, the search for the rude bits in the Bible, and the usual hair-raising revelations about where babies came from and how they got there.

Jeremy, who was beginning to achieve the success he required, took to coming back to school on Old Boys' Day. Never an academic success, he could not help but crow to himself that he now earned more money in six months than his old housemaster earned in a year. Benevolent swaggering was fun, especially since little Marion was getting pretty, with large eyes, shiny hair, and a small but perfectly formed body, and now added to her charms by adoring him.

Marion was eighteen when Jeremy decided to marry her. When he told her of this decision, she remained entirely silent. Could it be that she was going to say no? Jeremy was not accustomed to the word 'no' from women. For a moment, he wondered if perhaps he had better look elsewhere for a suitable wife. But then, to his surprise, he realised that he didn't want to do that.

In the silence that had intrigued her future husband, Marion was going through shock waves. It was as though a feast had been set before her, but she didn't know which fork to take, which glass to drink from. She was white with shyness, and her throat was dry. Not knowing what to do, she put out her hand. With it safely in Jeremy's, she reached up and kissed him. She would have gone to bed with him, then and there. But Jeremy had different ideas.

Jeremy was of the school that makes a sharp division between girls you knock off and girls you marry. It was as well that Marion, who owing to the limitations of her education had never jumped a vaulting-horse or played anything even remotely rough, was, on her wedding night, very obviously a virgin. For Jeremy was astounded at her passionate reception of his cautious and tender honeymoon advances.

The first year of her marriage, spent in a flat just off Sloane Square, was the happiest year of Marion's life. She had never lived in London, and it was bliss. The King's Road was filled with noisy, dashing, glamorous people, and Jeremy had given her an account at Peter Jones.

Each morning, Jeremy would sit on the edge of the bed to tie up his shoelaces. 'Don't get up, darling,' he would say, his weight practically shaking her out on to the floor. But she always did; she liked to get his breakfast. Waking in the morning, watching Jeremy shave, watching him tie his tie, watching him shake the shower-drops off his curly hair all over the glass top of her dressing table was, for her, a sort of after-orgasm, an extension of the night in bed.

'Men,' she would cluck, wiping spots off the dressing table, picking up Jeremy's wet towel, and straightening the curtains he clumsily tossed back from the rail, every morning.

Jeremy was equally happy. 'Women,' he would say, looking with pretended rue at Marion's purchases from Peter Jones, on his return from the City. 'What is it today?'

Brocade cushions, little tables, a padded bedhead, coloured sheets to add to the already ample pile of wedding-present linen in the cupboard. Jeremy already felt pretty grown-up at twenty-five, but Marion, spending money with confidence for the first time in her life, confirmed his position as a young man doing very well indeed.

The only person not so pleased was the married woman whose love affair with Jeremy had now been discontinued. For Jeremy, his marriage now so happily jelled, said to Marion, 'It's time we started a baby, don't you think?' He equated starting a baby with fidelity, at least for the time being.

Marion had never been on the pill. The pill, in Jeremy's opinion, was for the other sort of woman. He had no intention of allowing alien chemicals to enter his wife's body. To give her a few months in which to learn about marriage, he had escorted her to a reliable, ageing, female gynaecologist who still provided the elsewhere outmoded diaphragm.

The Dutch cap went into the dustbin and the young couple anticipated an early result. Peter Jones now saw Marion hovering in the cot department rather than in the occasional-table-and-magazine-rack department.

They were only mildly disappointed to find out that one wishfully missed period does not a pregnancy make. So far, Jeremy's marrying of her had given Marion a considerable sense of success. But, as the months went by and no baby showed willingness, she drooped. The slimness and slight build that had endeared her to Jeremy now looked, to him, like thinness. She must see a doctor.

Knowing himself to be the only man to have explored her little body, a fact of which he was touchingly proud, he took her back to the same gynaecologist. Herself a grandmother, the old doctor, who was generous with her time, concluded her clinical examination and then made Marion sit still, in a comfortable chair. 'Nothing wrong with your innards,' she said, settling her capacious bosom on her desk. 'A slightly retroverted uterus, but that often happens to girls with ardent husbands. Lucky you. It'll probably right itself but, if it doesn't, we can give you a little anaesthetic and a big shove.'

'How will I know?' asked Marion, her fists clenched.

'You won't. I will. Give yourself three months and then come back to me. Meanwhile, relax and enjoy yourself. Relaxation, that's the ticket. My dear child, I cried my head off when my first baby didn't turn up as ordered, and me a doctor! But she came along when she wanted to. Oh, another thing: it wouldn't hurt you to put on a bit of weight. I don't often have to say that, these days. When I was first in practice, I saw more malnutrition than obesity. I'm not going to weigh you, I can see with my own two eyes that you are underweight. Put on half a stone, like a good girl, and come back and see me in three months.'

In three months, Marion was neither pregnant nor any heavier. The 'little anaesthetic and big shove' took place in a private hospital. 'You'll be fine now,' said the gynaecologist. 'A wee bit tender, just for a few days.'

Jeremy, desperately sorry for his aching and bleeding wife, lay beside her in bed, scarcely daring to touch her. Marion longed to be stroked and petted but Jeremy was afraid to do it. He knew how easily his desires were aroused.

'Oh,' said the married woman, answering her doorbell and finding Jeremy on the step. 'Long time no see. And what brings you here?'

'I was just passing, and I wondered how you were. How are you, Liz?'

'The name is Lisa, in case you've forgotten. How about pissing off?'

'All right. If you say so.'

'Oh, come in, damn and blast you.'

Lisa had no *tendresse* for Jeremy. She was a randy realist, with a husband to whom she was faithful, in her way. Her way did not include sexual faithfulness, since this was not required. Dear William was high on brains, books and generosity, but low on testosterone. At five o'clock in the afternoon, throats would be clearing either in the London Library or the British Museum, as William was politely heaved out. Then he would wander down to the Adelphi, drink a few glasses of wine and discuss the meaning of protons with thin men.

'I do like a good fuck,' said Lisa, in bed with Jeremy. 'Well done.' Truth to tell, Jeremy hadn't done all that well. One of the nice things about Jeremy, she remembered from the days before he was married, was that he was a great kisser, and not at all shy about where he kissed. It was as well she was an amateur, rather than a professional, whore. Her own enthusiasm would have worn her into the ground in a week, had she been obliged to make a living out of it.

'Sorry, darling, but I'll have to throw you out. William will be home soon.'

'What would happen if he walked in here now?' Jeremy asked.

'He wouldn't. He's far too polite. It's not that. It's just that he always forgets to eat and I want to make some chicken soup for him.'

Jeremy went home to the flat, wondering why he simply hadn't enjoyed himself with Lisa. Perhaps he felt guilty about being unfaithful to Marion? But, after all, in the years between deciding to marry her and actually doing so, to which he was most certainly committed, he had very happily continued to burst into many a bedroom.

Marion was reading a cookery book. He kissed her. He thought 'Ah, so that's it. It's wanting a baby that's doing this to me. I want a legitimate son. Daughters, too, of course.'

A few days later, flipping through *Country Life* while at the dentist's, Jeremy saw for sale a house in a place called Swanmere. That was the answer. It was simple. For his part, he could cope with the pace of London life but, quite clearly, Marion must be removed from the bump and bustle of the King's Road. Unconsciously echoing the views of his father-in-law, he decided on a quiet life for his wife and children. Never a man to hang about, he rang the estate agent who advertised in *Country Life* and bought Swanmere Cottage. The estate agent nearly had a heart attack. Never before had he concluded a sale so easily or so rapidly.

Village life would suit Marion. Of course it would: it suited Jeremy, so it followed that it would suit Marion. Jeremy engaged, on weekends, rapidly and ebulliently in village life. Swanmere Cottage was a big house, and Jeremy did debate changing its humble name. But it appeared that the name 'cottage' was not so humble. Only the Manor was above it.

Its timbers had come from the Manor's park, and it had been lived in for more than three hundred years by dowagers and younger sons, esquires. As there were a couple of acres of land with Swanmere Cottage, Jeremy, whose education had been paid for by the profits of trade rather than inherited wealth or title, enjoyed doing what he thought best for his little wife and, at the same time, gaining the gratifying right to call himself Jeremy Clark, Esq.

It turned out that Marion did fit well into Swanmere life. Friendly Swanmere welcomed the young Clarks. Jeremy was popular in the Beaters' Arms. He played good cricket and put away his pints like a man. And Marion, who was regarded with brief suspicion, having come down from London, was soon seen to be a nice young woman who had been born in the country. Not here, but good enough.

Laura Fenby was expecting Luke, when the Clarks arrived. Marion, however slim her own figure and however smart her clothes, envied her.

It was Marion who got Swanmere Cottage together. She was confident in her ability to organise a slatted linen cupboard, and fill it with tidily folded towels, sheets, table-cloths, linen napkins ironed and folded, and, to one side, the little cot-covers she had bought. Otherwise, her efforts were entirely dictated by magazines, Peter Jones and what she hoped Jeremy would like.

But as the months went by, however much she became a Swanmere wife, she did not become a Swanmere mother.

She went back to the elderly gynaecologist, who still said, leaning her even vaster bust on the desk, 'Babies come when babies come. However, we have to recognise modern research. You have got to conceive at the right time. Ovulation, that's the thing. Now, here's what you do. You take your temperature, rectally, every morning. Be careful, don't break the thermometer up your bum. But your temperature goes up to just under a hundred when you are ovulating. So make love then. Oh dear,' she said, laughing, 'I make love sound like a board meeting with no clothes on, don't I?'

'Oh no,' said Marion, politely, 'Jeremy likes making love. He makes me very happy. It's the best part of my life. I'm very tidy, you see. Sometimes I think I fuss too much. But it's different when I'm in bed with Jeremy.'

'Good, good. That's very good. But it brings me to another point. You're obviously close to your husband. I think you should get him to come and see me.'

'About me?'

'No. About him. I really ought to check his sperm count. There's nothing to it, you know!' She was about to follow up with the explanation that infertility and impotence are two different things, and that a man can be a perfectly good lover and yet short of sperm.

But Marion spoke first. 'I have to tell you something very private. Jeremy confided in me.' Oh heavens, thought the doctor, not gonorrhoea, I hope. 'You see, he had a lot of, well, you know, he slept with lots of girls before we were married.'

'Good, good. Nothing worse than a fumbler.'

'But there was one in particular. Poor Jeremy, he didn't realise she was in love with him. He's never quite forgiven himself. He'd already decided to marry me, when it happened. He made her pregnant. She wanted to have the baby. She wanted him to marry her. She worked in a shop.'

'I see. How long ago did this happen?'

'Just before we were married. He'd already bought my wedding ring. He didn't tell me till after we were married. Poor darling, he was afraid it might put me off.'

'I see. So that's definite, then. Proved at stud. What happened to the baby?'

'That's the awful thing. He made her have an abortion. And it was my fault.'

'How could it be your fault?'

'Because he was determined to marry me. And Jeremy, well, Jeremy brought me to life.' The old doctor kept her mouth shut on the subject of the sacrifice of the shopgirl and her baby. Marion drew breath. 'He taught me all about making love. I want to give him children.'

'You will,' said the old doctor. 'There's nothing amiss with you, and apparently, from what you have told me, nothing amiss with him. Your uterus is in position now, so that's all right.'

Marion went home and tidied the linen cupboard.

And now, twenty years after her wedding day, the builders were putting in a third bathroom. Jeremy was in London and wouldn't be back until late.

After the builders had at last gone, she walked into her dining room, and thought about redecorating it. The red and gold which Jeremy had liked – they often had friends of his, from the City, to stay, and the décor suited cigars, smoked after several courses of trusted, expensive recipes painstakingly read and followed by Marion – looked dark on this bright April morning. She wished she had Laura Fenby's talent for giving a casual, jolly party. Maybe she should re-do the dining room in a paler colour: perhaps aquamarine.

In the linen cupboard, cot-sheets and tiny covers had long been buried under a new set of linen table-napkins. It was half-past three. 'We're off now,' called out Mr Bagshot. 'Got nicely started. But I'll have to go to the wholesaler's, if you want those gold taps. May take a while.'

She folded in the edges of the dust-sheets, concealing the detritus. There wasn't much point in doing any more. She went back down to her wild garden. The sky had clouded over. It was growing cold. A bird flew low, on its last search of the day for something to eat. Some of last autumn's crab apples still clung to their tree. A wind rustled by, and one apple fell. And then all was silence.

Jeremy wouldn't be home until late. She left the garden

and went indoors, to make him something for dinner. She washed the builders' footmarks off the kitchen floor, and put the discarded saucepans into the dustbin. 'What a chump I am,' she said. 'But still, poor saucepans, I'd rather you went out clean than dirty.'

3

'I'm going over to play at Marion's,' said Judy Fenby, aged eight. All the children called Marion 'Marion', and never 'Mrs Clark'. Marion was glad: it gave her the feeling of being young enough still to have children of her own.

To Peter, Judy, Ann and Luke, it was like having a young and pretty aunt. And Jeremy, when they saw him, was sort of uncle-ish. They had no aunts or uncles of their own, with Mummy having no brothers or sisters and Daddy with only a married sister in Canada, who sent presents but whom they had never met, and a brother referred to as 'poor Tom', who lived in a place called the Far East, and didn't send presents. Daddy's parents were dead, so they just had Granny and Grandpa Chadwick. They liked Grandpa quite well – he let them use his big books to build bridges – and they believed they liked Granny. Granny had told them they loved her. On their brief visits to Mummy and Daddy's mummy and daddy, Veronica would rush them out to buy ice-creams, and then, more likely than not, forget to give them any supper. But of aunts they knew nothing.

'You can come with me, if you like,' Judy now said to Ann.

Laura, knowing that Ann would trot along wherever Judy decided, looked up from feeding Luke, while she and Mrs Bean were having their morning coffee. 'Be careful, crossing the road,' she said.

'Oh, Mummy, we're not *babies*,' said Ann.

Laura, saying 'Don't get in Marion's way, if she's busy.

And wipe your shoes on the mat,' was glad to see them go. Luke was a much easier baby than Peter or even the girls had been. He was a big smiler but an even bigger eater. Given the opportunity, he would suck all day long. As he never had colic, and never threw up, Laura found it easier to let him have his bossy way. She had, on more than one occasion, found herself stirring soup with Luke tucked inside her milk-spotted jersey. She had thought that breast-feeding the new baby might be an opportunity to begin explaining the facts of life to her little girls.

'Yeuk,' said Judy.

'He smells,' said Ann. She didn't really mind the foody smell of her baby brother, in fact she secretly liked it. But what Judy said, went.

Luke, who was benevolent about the service available, merrily took it in at one end and let it out at the other. At well over a year old, he planned to continue with this arrangement. And, dear little man as he was, he had just discovered that crawling and staggering are more enjoyable if you get rid of your nappy. He cheerfully caused a good deal of wiping up. Linoleum or carpet made no difference to him.

'Now, your Peter,' said Mrs Bean, stirring her coffee vigorously, 'he was different again. No bother with him; always a nice clean nappy.'

'He was difficult to feed, though,' said Laura. They both laughed as Luke staggered up on to Mrs Bean's lap.

'Hard luck, Lukey,' said Mrs Bean. 'You got the wrong mummy.'

'A-A-,' said Luke.

'He means Ann,' said Laura. 'Ann's gone to see Marion, darling. So has Judy. They'll be back later. Now look, if it's all right with you, I'm going to put a clean nappy on you.' It always made Mrs Bean laugh, the way Mrs Fenby would talk to Luke as though he could understand every word.

'How's Peter getting on?' asked Mrs Bean. She did not at all disapprove of sending little boys away to boarding-school.

Given the chance, she would have been only too happy to have done the same with hers. But she had had to put her arms round Laura, the day Peter, skinny in his oversized uniform, had been driven away by Mr Fenby, to start his first term at prep school.

'All right,' said Laura. 'You know, I think he actually likes it. The girls were a bit much for him. I was amazed, how quickly he settled in. The first thing he said was, "You know, Mummy, boys don't touch other boys' things." He'd got a little cupboard, beside his bed, and so had all the others, you see. I gathered that whatever they keep in them is private, and woe betide any boy who opens another boy's cupboard.'

Mrs Bean chuckled. 'Chance would be a fine thing, for us mothers, wouldn't it. Lucky Peter.'

The two little girls knocked on Marion Clark's front door. 'Are you busy? Mummy said we weren't to come in if you were busy.'

'Not at all. Just a tick while I put the Hoover away.'

'Mummy never Hoovers. Mrs Bean does it,' said Judy.

Jeremy had wanted Marion to have a cleaner, but she refused, point-blank. What else had she to do, all day, but use her one skill, which was to create order? It was the best she could give. Now, she was glad to see Judy and Ann. They always, Judy in particular, made her feel good about the house she cleaned so meticulously. After all, she could hardly expect Jeremy, who had never seen his house less than impeccable, to come bounding through the door in the evening and burst into songs of praise over the cleanliness of the downstairs loo.

'I say, Marion,' said Judy, 'isn't this new? I haven't seen this before.'

'This' was a Steuben glass vase Jeremy had brought back from a business visit to New York. 'Jeremy gave it to me,' said Marion. She cast round in her mind, to think if she had anything in the house Judy and Ann would like to eat. The freezer was well stocked, but she had not thought of getting anything out for this evening. Jeremy was staying over for the night, in London. The chaps he played cricket with, and downed pints with at the Beaters' Arms, on weekends, had no idea how seriously hard this jolly fellow worked.

'You are lucky,' said Judy, 'Jeremy's always giving you presents. May I get the silver box out?' The silver box was a shining treasure Judy loved to be allowed to take out of the glass-fronted cabinet. 'Don't touch it, Ann,' she said bossily. 'You've got grubby hands. It was very expensive; Jeremy bought it specially for Marion.' Ann sniffed, left Judy with the box, and went out into the garden, where she tripped over the edge of the patio.

Marion, finding the child lying on the ground, covered in mud, was afraid she might have hurt herself. She sat beside her and took her in her arms. 'Are you all right?' she asked.

'Perfectly, thank you. I like it, out here. Tell you what, though, I'd like a biscuit. I'm hungry. Judy never is, she's slimming. She wants to look like you.'

Marion stood up and let the child run into the house. Finding biscuits helped to take her mind off other things.

At about eight o'clock that evening, Jeremy, whose morning shave had long turned to stubble, was watching three computer screens at a time when he became aware of a colleague's nudge and voice. 'I'm knocking off. I've had enough.'

'Oh, Rodney. OK.'

'You're not going home tonight, are you? Neither am I. Julia's got her horses, so she's quite happy. I bought the bloody animals for her, let's face it. Come on, let's go. Let's find a couple of birds and make an evening of it.'

'No, thanks all the same. You go. I'll stick around. I want to see what comes in from Japan. And I've got a feeling in my fingertips about Korea.'

'Money isn't everything,' said Rodney, having made quite enough of the stuff to make such remarks with impunity. He left, in search of an opportunity to spend quite a lot of it on what he regarded as enjoyment.

Jeremy dined alone, got a bit drunk alone, and then slept alone in the company flat. Having made love at the right time, he was not going to touch Marion for at least the next two weeks. He feared to burst the fragile bubble that they both hoped so much was forming inside her.

Avoiding infidelity, almost superstitiously, Jeremy had become irritable at home. It didn't occur to him that Marion, too, was frustrated. To make matters worse, by the time the dreary evidence of 'not this time' had come and gone, Jeremy's libido had reached the proportions of a bursting boil. One heaving grunt and Marion was left to lie awake all night, or sometimes to walk about the house, bent double by aching desire and shame. Twofold shame: first in her disappointment at Jeremy's now terse embraces, and second in her failure to conceive for him.

It never occurred to her to explain any of this to her husband. Her upbringing precluded any such notion. She was quite unaware that her teenage years were on a par with those of a Victorian girl.

The only sex education she had ever had came from her father's maid-of-all-work, a kindly woman who had once walked out with an under-gardener, although it had come to nothing, and she had never married. Even so, seeing as how Sir had no idea, Hetty had given Marion, as the motherless child approached twelve years old, a few veiled explanations. Hetty's description of what a girl might expect when she became a married woman was about as helpful as her asseveration that Mummy had gone to Heaven.

All Marion knew about sex was that it had been something absolutely lovely, when she and Jeremy were first married. And now it wasn't, and the last thing in the world she was capable of was to say so to her husband.

4

'It's very sweet of you to invite me to lunch, Marion,' said Mrs Chadwick. 'Such a pretty dining room. Indeed, I don't mind telling you, it's a pleasure to eat in a civilised manner.' She unfolded one of Marion's linen napkins, ironed but not starched.

His mother-in-law's arrival to live at the Grange was a first for John Fenby, in that it was the first time in their entire married life that Laura had refused to be advised by him. 'I can't say no. How can I? She is my mother, after all. And she knows we've got plenty of room, now that the children have all left home.'

'But darling, think!'

Which is exactly what Laura didn't want to do. She had never permitted herself to delve under the surface of her relationship with her mother. As a child, rather fearing her, and yet under her spell, she had fallen into the way of always trying to please – to be 'Mummy's good little girl'. Being an only child, she was not only sole target, but had the added disadvantage of no siblings with whom to compare notes.

Veronica Chadwick, at eighty years old, was still capable of being charming. People would say, in her hearing, 'Isn't Veronica wonderful? And still beautiful; she must have been absolutely stunning as a girl.' But as there was no one still living who had known her then, the question of whether she had always been an untruthful bully, or had become one, was hidden by the mists of time.

Had she dared to be more observant as a child and a growing girl, Laura would have known herself to be the offspring of a disastrous marriage. For her father, lost in awe of his luck in marrying the beautiful Veronica, had no idea how to handle her. His love-making was timid, romantic and respectful.

Veronica had had no doubts at all about marrying Richard Chadwick. What she saw in him was exactly what she wanted. He was well bred, a major in a good regiment, his promotion as a regular officer speeded up by the war. Although she had plenty of suitors, she allowed no liberties. Wartime or no wartime, Veronica was a determined 'save-it-for-marriage' girl. In all fairness, it was a genuine principle on her part, brought up as she had been to consider marriage, and a good marriage at that, the only career for a girl. It was a principle that had begun to backfire, in those heady days, and she had had to endure the turning away of some of her admirers, in the direction of more up-to-date young women. In the nick of time, Richard Chadwick entered the lists, and soon won his fair lady.

Having only the haziest notion of what to expect on her honeymoon, she had found the actual fact of it dull, and rather embarrassing. Completely unaroused, even more embarrassing than the messy business itself was that it was accompanied by Richard's outpourings of words of love, words that sounded simply silly to her, as she lay under his body.

She had thoroughly enjoyed the courtship. Richard's adoring behaviour, especially in public, had been sweet. She even felt quite sentimental herself, dancing cheek to cheek at the Savoy, with her solitaire diamond on the pretty white finger that rested on his uniformed shoulder for all to see.

But marriage? Once achieved, marriage was a ghastly flop. Having no ability to see any point of view but her own, Veronica had little sympathy for the husband who, on his short honeymoon leave, implored her to love him.

32

Laura's birth was a difficult one, or so Veronica claimed. Even on embarkation leave, before his posting to India, Richard was not allowed into her bed. Though uncertain whether this was due to the dreadful pain of the birth, or the fear of a further pregnancy in his absence on the service of his King and Country, he bore it with a fortitude which was to inform his later years with Veronica.

It was during the early years of Laura's life that the pattern was cut for what was now about to happen. For Veronica, bypassing her husband, traded in her previous role of prettiest girl and sweet fiancée, for that of charming mother of her dear little girl. Somehow, even in those difficult days of the late forties and early fifties, Veronica managed to dress her daughter in smocked Liberty prints and little tweed coats from Hayfords, with embroidered shantung collars. And, for parties, bronze slippers with pom-poms and criss-cross elastic to hold them in place over the silk socks with clocks.

In spite of the loss of her baby front teeth, Laura remained a sufficiently attractive child to be still the apple of her mother's eye. But the onset of adolescence was a different thing. Overnight, Veronica found herself terrified by the advent of another woman in her house. Her way of handling this was simple. Boarding-school. Laura wept tears of homesickness, and missed Mummy. She missed her because, quite simply, the trap had long been sprung.

To do Veronica justice, she really had no idea of what she had done to her daughter. Had she married a different husband, she might have been a nicer person. It was not her fault that she began the road to a way of life she learned to achieve by arranging that *nothing* was her fault.

'Poor Mummy,' said Laura. 'It's so lonely for her, since Daddy died.'

Indeed, Richard Chadwick dead had awakened a love in his widow akin to that she had shown him when a fiancée. 'Poor Veronica,' it was said, 'she is absolutely heartbroken, lost without Richard.' And Laura, reverting to her infant indoctrination, was swept along, even erasing her own knowledge of her mother's mid-life sexual shenanigans. Now, Daddy had died a beloved husband and not the cuckold the unfortunate man had really been.

John Fenby's rearguard action was finally defeated by his fair-minded acceptance that, until now, Laura had never gone against his wishes. He also went against his own better judgement, which was that there had always been something about his mother-in-law that he didn't much like, telling himself that it would be a sad business if, after his own demise, his own sons and daughters should refuse to take care of *their* mother. Thus, Veronica was installed.

Marion was torn between loyalty to Laura, whose mother was even now toying with shrimps in aspic, and falling for the charm Mrs Chadwick well knew how to exert when she wished to. Luckily she was not obliged to speak, as Veronica Chadwick could, and did, speak for two. 'Oh, dear Laura does her best,' she said, wiping her wrinkled lips with a linen napkin, 'and John puts up with anything, of course.'

'He loves her,' said Marion.

Mrs Chadwick did not hear that remark. 'But we have dinner at the kitchen table. Well, dinner? One course and cheese. I call that supper. Oh, how nice, you've made these meringues yourself.' She tucked in, greedily. Now that she was eighty, Veronica Chadwick's long-ago exploits with the window-cleaner, the gardener, and with the double-glazing salesman, come to that, were quite forgotten, substituted by greed for food. She poured cream. 'And always so *late*,' she continued. 'Laura has no idea of punctuality. Oh dear, sometimes I think I made a dreadful mistake. I only sold my house to help her.' Veronica had sold the house for a great deal of money, as soon as her husband was in his grave.

Marion had fallen into the way of having Veronica over to lunch or tea at least once a week. She was well aware of the old woman's blatant selfishness but, not being her daughter, she was able to find it quite funny. And it helped Laura, and gave her something useful to do. It wasn't difficult. You only had to plug into a safe subject, and Veronica would be off. She did not need a post-prandial nap.

Marion made coffee and served it with *petits fours*. 'How are the children?' she asked. She knew perfectly well how they were. Judy was in London, making a successful career as a public relations executive, but dismissed by her grandmother as 'being a secretary'. By the same token, Peter's job, which he loathed, in an insurance office, was called 'doing very well in an excellent position'. Ann was a pudding chef (she had always liked sweet things) in a country hotel where she cohabited cheerfully with the *chef de legumes*. Luke was a little harder to describe in Chadwickese, as Veronica had no definition for what Luke was up to, which was to enjoy himself thoroughly, picking up any old job when he needed some money, and then doing it for the shortest possible time.

Veronica sipped her coffee. Marion, feeling the need of a brandy herself, offered it. 'Have you any Cointreau?' asked Veronica. Of course she had, Jeremy always kept the drinks cupboard stocked with everything anyone could desire. 'The children? Well, Luke you must often see. He's always coming home. Well, whenever he wants something. Laura spoilt him, of course. He takes complete advantage of her, and she lets him.' A skilled advantage-taker herself, Veronica Chadwick took every opportunity of driving a wedge between jolly, naughty Luke and the mother he loved.

Marion began to wish it was time for Veronica to go. She had, over the years, grown accustomed to spending a lot of time by herself. Jeremy had become someone she knew occasionally in bed, but mostly in the company of dinner party guests. He was a genial and generous host, and never failed, at some point during an evening, to put his arm affectionately round his pretty wife, in front of everybody. In fact, it was almost always after one of the Clarks' renowned dinner parties that Jeremy would make love to her. She had long given up on the temperature-taking. She seldom felt passionate these days. But Jeremy, large and curly, slightly but good-naturedly drunk, liked to round out a good evening.

Now, it had become Marion's way to put her house in order in the morning and then to spend her afternoons in the garden. She hoped Veronica would not ask to be shown round the garden. She hated showing people round her garden. She need not have worried. Veronica had no such thing in mind. What she did have in mind, Marion resigned herself to, was staying on for tea. And going on talking.

'Your mother died when you were quite a child, didn't she?' asked Veronica. The question was preparation for a statement. She swept on inexorably. 'That must have been dreadful for you. At least poor Laura has always had me. I would have been much more comfortable in a nice flat, with what's left of my own precious things about me. But you see, she's my only child. And I must do what I think best for her. Such a pity you didn't have children.'

'Yes,' was all Marion could bring herself to say.

Veronica sighed. 'Well, no disappointments, that way. Talking of which, Peter's coming home this weekend. He's broken up with Deirdre, or whatever her name is.'

Marion sipped brandy and adopted a leaning-forward posture. That way, she could doze with her eyes open, undetected by Veronica. Somewhere along the line, she left the room and made tea. Veronica was talking as she left, and talking as she got back. But at last the subject of Ann's unsuitable liaison with a young man who, according to Veronica 'peeled potatoes. *Really*, I ask you!' drifted to a finish and Veronica departed. Marion went out into her garden.

By now, it was five o'clock. Laura's relief at having her mother out of the house for a couple of hours had given way to guilty anxiety. She wouldn't have dreamt of thinking that a telephone call from Marion to break the news to her that

Mummy had keeled over and died at the luncheon table would be salvation.

'Where are you?' called Veronica, letting herself in at the front door. Laura had scuttled into the kitchen. Quite ridiculously, she always hoped to be found by Mother, in the act of doing something useful. She peeled a courgette until nothing was left of it. 'What *are* you doing?' asked Veronica.

'Getting dinner.'

'Don't bother, for me. Marion gave me a delicious luncheon. I must say, *she* always takes a lot of trouble.' Veronica had a talent, second to none, for crushing.

'I was beginning to worry about you. You were quite a long time away.'

'*I* didn't want to stay out so long,' said Veronica in pained tones. 'In fact, I'm tired out. I only stayed to let you have some time to yourself. I don't like to be in the way.'

Laura found herself, as usual, grovelling. And lying. 'Really, Mummy, how can you say such a thing? You know I love having you here. We all do.'

Pressing home her advantage, Veronica continued. 'You can give me some supper in bed.' She loved supper in bed, a ceremony that involved at least three journeys upstairs for someone, usually Laura, to bring the salt, a clean napkin and, invariably, after insisting upon the tininess of her appetite, just a little more of the fish. But now she said, 'I don't like going to bed early, I sleep so badly. But it will give you and John the chance to talk without me in the way.'

Deciding that she would scream if she didn't immediately have a cigarette, Laura said, 'I'll just go and empty the compost bucket.' Mummy always burst out coughing almost before lighter flame touched cigarette. Out in the garden, where a sharp little wind had sprung up, she observed, aloud, 'Smokers don't die of lung cancer. They die of pneumonia.' Playing hookey, she lit another cigarette and put Mummy, for the moment, out of her mind.

She always worried about Peter. A first child gets the

amateur mother. On the one hand, she had been pleased that he settled into school so well; on the other, she feared it was her own inadequacy that made school seem so satisfactory. And now Peter was coming home for the weekend, without Deirdre. When told of this, Veronica had made up her mind that the couple had split up. Peter and Deirdre had not split up. In fact, only a couple of days ago, he had been with her to the Register Office, to book a wedding date.

They had been living together for over a year. Although he had been working in London for quite a long time, he had never, until Deirdre came into his life, had any desire to find a place of his own to live in. He was, at this time, occupying the spare room of a house owned by a colleague and his wife. They were a monumentally dull couple who had bought a house in a rising suburb that failed to rise.

Almost everyone at Peter's place of business was dull; the duller for not believing themselves to be. By contrast, Deirdre was a figure of glamour. Having learned to be chic, she was able to give an impression of prettiness.

She was the Managing Director's secretary. The eldest of three sisters, brought up in Leeds by decent but drearily poor parents, she had left school at sixteen, and had no qualifications of any kind, and no secretarial training. So it says a good deal for her presence of mind and eye for clothes that she had managed to walk into the position she now occupied.

And Deirdre now possessed a flat. The Managing Director, who had hit on the bright idea of working after hours, had actually bought her a small but perfectly formed nest on Chelsea Reach. There was only one small misunderstanding. Deirdre, whose family might be poor but were proud of being extremely respectable – indeed both her younger sisters had been married before their children were born – believed that, at the age of twenty-seven, she was going to be the wife of the Managing Director. Her younger sisters might have married before her, but not half as well as she intended to do.

Unfortunately, she had reckoned without the existing Mrs Managing Director. Having lived a very long time with a husband who was apt to get silly, she had rapidly and shrewdly recognised that he was At It again.

Working after hours was abruptly brought to a close. Having bought and paid for the flat, the Managing Director considered himself lucky to get away with merely handing it over, lock, stock and lease, to Deirdre.

Deirdre did her best to keep her end up with her younger sisters. She had a smart flat in the smartest part of London. But they, thinking little of London, failed to be impressed.

It was at this moment that Peter came her way. Quiet, bespectacled, courteous and nice, Peter Fenby was not a man to sweep a girl off her feet. Deirdre had no wish to be swept off her feet. What she needed was to get her life in order.

The opportunity came at the office Christmas party. This year, the Managing Director's wife put in an appearance. As a result, Deirdre's erstwhile supporter studiously avoided her. She was genuinely miserable and not far off panic when Peter chose the moment to say 'May I get you a drink?' A dazzling smile was his reward.

Everyone was drinking a lot, and Peter was striving to do the same. So far it hadn't seemed to cheer him, and all he could think about was the dismal prospect of making his way back to his lonely, cold room in a house that smelt of deadly efforts to make a trendy stuffing for the turkey.

His first night at Deirdre's flat was spent sleeping on the sofa. He had simply accepted her kind offer to spare him a tedious journey. After that, they separated briefly, each to go home for Christmas and Boxing Days. He went back to his lodging, but very soon moved in with Deirdre, this time into her bed.

Now, he had been there for thirteen months, during which time Deirdre had been very good to him. It was nice to have his shirts ironed and his socks paired up. He took to doing quite a lot of the cooking, which was homely and cosy.

They were already living like a married couple, not like people having a passionate affair. So, when Deirdre intimated that their union should be regularised, it was the proper thing to do. Not for nothing had Peter inherited from his father a sense of what was honourable in a man.

It was decided that Deirdre should go home to Leeds, and give her family their news, while Peter went down to Swanmere, to do the same by his.

On the Friday before going down to Swanmere, Peter, face to face with his computer in his insurance office, wondered why he was so miserably unhappy. At the station, with half an hour to wait before his train, he went into the bar and ordered a large Scotch. This had a wonderfully cheering effect. As there was a mobile bar on the train, he had the same again and decided that, once they were married, he would explain to Deirdre that he was bored to death with his job, and longed to do something completely different, even though he wasn't sure what. She would understand.

John Fenby, meeting the train, thought Peter looked tired. It must be hell working in London, and he was thankful he had never had to do so himself. A large whisky, in his opinion, was what the boy needed, he thought as he clapped Peter on the shoulder and pushed him into the car for the drive home. 'We're here, darling,' he called to Laura.

'Lovely.' Laura rushed out of the kitchen, and also thought Peter looked tired. 'Supper's nearly ready,' she said, kissing him.

'Give us time for a drink,' said John.

As Laura returned to the kitchen, Veronica, who had heard the car, made her way downstairs in pink. 'Sherry, Veronica?' asked John.

'No dear, don't open the sherry just for me. I'll have what you're having.'

The spaghetti Laura had made was actually delicious, and Peter's favourite. Veronica, managing to toy disdainfully but at the same time swallowing a large quantity, paused only to say, 'Well, Peter, so Deirdre is not with you! I hope all is well.'

Watching her son's face, Laura served second helpings. 'There's lemon meringue pie for afters. Marion Clark made it for me, when she heard you were coming down, Peter.'

'Marion is always so kind,' said Veronica. 'She seems, for some strange reason, to have become very fond of me. She lost her own mother at an early age; so sad.'

Laura served the pie, and John produced a good Sauternes to go with it. Peter took one forkful of pie and one sip of the sweet wine, and Laura thought he looked as though he was going to be sick. But Veronica ate and drank, now successfully deflected from the subject of Deirdre.

At bedtime, Laura wordlessly put her arms round Peter and held him tight. Peter hugged her back, and was kissed goodnight. He slept well. Laura lay awake for a long time.

5

Towards dawn, Laura fell into the sort of sleep that only brings anxious, uneasy dreams.

When, at last, she came fully awake, she lay and worried about Peter. She knew that last night's hugs and kisses, genuine as they were, had only been made possible for Peter by his having a lot to drink. He would be, this morning, his usual uncommunicative self, back to answers of 'Yes' or 'No' to any question she asked him.

It had never been easy for Laura to talk to Peter. At first, she had thought perhaps that this was just the way of boys. But that idea had been dispelled by Luke, who had always been cheerfully open, falling about with rude giggles and shameless jokes.

John, beside her, woke up. He leaned over and kissed her, stroking her face. She smiled at him, as best she could. 'What time is it?' she asked. 'I'll have to get up in a minute.'

'Surely,' said John, 'Veronica doesn't have to have breakfast in bed every morning? She's not an invalid.'

'I can't stop doing it, now.'

'Why not? You give in to her the entire time.'

'John, it's easier that way.' This was the nearest she dared come to an admission that having her mother to live in their house was a mistake; the cringing, weak-minded mistake of a daughter who has inherited her father's gentlemanly genes, rather than her mother's alley-cat survival kit.

'Not in the long run,' said John.

'It's all very well for you. You just get out of the way,

except for meals.' Laura knew she was going to start snapping at John: it seemed to have been happening ever since her mother had moved in. She got up, grabbed some clothes, and dressed in the bathroom.

After breakfast, she rang Marion to thank her for the lemon meringue pie. 'Would you and Jeremy like to come to supper tonight?' she asked. 'It would be nice for Peter, it would take him out of himself.'

'We're free, all right,' said Marion, 'but why don't you come to us, instead? I've nothing to do all day, and you've got a houseful.'

'Oh, Marion, I ought to say no. I'm sure it's your turn to come to us. But could we really?'

'Of course. At least it will save you cooking one meal. And before you ask me not to fuss, I won't, but I will, if you see what I mean. I like making something nice for my friends.'

Before lunch, John took Peter down to the Beaters' Arms for a beer. Veronica wandered into the kitchen as Laura was washing salad and putting slices of cold ham on to plates. Before her mother could turn up her nose, Laura said in the bright, over-decibelled voice she seemed to use far too often these days, 'We're just having salad for lunch, Mummy. Marion has asked us all to dinner, and you know how much you enjoy her food.'

'No salad for me, if you please. Just a little bread and butter and not too much ham. It's so salty. Where is Peter?'

'He and John have gone to the pub for a beer.'

'That's nice. It's high time they had a man-to-man talk. Maybe we shall find out what is going on between him and Deirdre.'

'Maybe.' Laura lit a cigarette. Damn it all, this was her own kitchen.

Veronica refrained from coughing. Even though she could see that Laura was in 'one of her moods' she could not help but make a performance out of the simple act of not coughing. She changed tack. 'It's simply that I worry about the boy. I only want him to be happy. I've only ever wanted you to be happy.'

Unable to think of a reply to this remark, Laura merely said, 'Goodness, this compost bucket's full.' Fortunately it was, having been topped up by the remains of Peter's uneaten lemon meringue pie, and also her own portion. 'I'll just empty it. I won't be a minute.'

It did only take a moment, and Laura had, all too soon, to return to fencing with her mother. But at last the men reappeared, and lunch was eaten.

Sport on television got them through the afternoon. Laura dressed for dinner. She had lost weight, and was at least pleased to find that she could get comfortably into her good black frock again.

There were drinks before dinner, in the Clarks' drawing room. Marion, well prepared as she always was for dinner parties, sat with her pretty little legs crossed, beside Peter. Veronica joined Jeremy at the drinks table, enjoying a vivacious discussion as to what she would have. Laura sank down beside John, and sipped at a glass of sherry.

Jeremy was as glad of an evening with company as Laura was. For Jeremy now had a mistress. He had virtuously kept away from other women for a long time. When months of childlessness became years of childlessness, he had said to Marion, 'Let's look on the bright side, sweetheart. How many couples can make love without the bother of birth control? Come on, relax and enjoy it.' This was genuinely kind in him, since the barrenness of the wife he had so carefully chosen was a real blow. He had been so sure of getting a son and heir, and then a little girl to make a pet of. But Marion had changed.

Sometimes it was hard to remember her as the girl whose passion he had once been so proud of awakening. She never refused him. But she never laughed or squealed, either. She knew he liked to have his back scratched, after making love. She still did that, but he could feel her reminding her hand to do it.

Then, one day as he was walking down Regent Street, on the way to buy Marion a present at Liberty's, a voice called out, 'Well, hallo. Hallo, Jeremy. You don't recognise me, do you? It's Janet.'

'Good Lord. Well I never. How are you, Janet?'

'A lot older, I realise, since you didn't know me. Let's see, it must be twenty years. Oh dear, I'm quite a hag, aren't I?' The woman before him was no 'hag'. But she was a far cry from the imploring girl he had so long ago paid to get rid of the child he had begotten on her. She had the careless, casual grandeur that only goes with very expensive clothes. And he knew it took a very expensive hairdresser indeed to give a woman the look of having just got out of bed and lost her hairbrush.

He fell into step beside her, and they strolled down Regent Street, quite a head-turning couple. 'It *is* nice to see you,' said Janet. 'You haven't changed, except you're even better looking. Age may have improved you.'

'What about lunch?' said Jeremy.

'Some time?'

'Now. I wasn't going to bother with lunch, I'd only come out to buy my wife a present. But I've got time, if you have.'

'Sure. I'm a woman of no importance, with time on my hands. Where do you want to go?'

'Let's go to Rules.'

'Without a reservation?' Janet very much liked Jeremy's reply which was that, for him, no reservation was necessary.

It was a foregone conclusion that they would end up in bed. Janet raised an eyebrow as Jeremy ordered oysters, but no word of what was about to come was spoken. They were seated side by side. Jeremy told the waiter to leave the wine for him to pour, which gave him the opportunity of subtly touching Janet's breast each time he filled her glass. After lunch, they were silent in the taxi and silent as they entered Janet's flat. And, still in silence, they walked together into the bedroom, dropping clothes as they went.

What followed was not love, but it was fun. Jeremy had not had fun in bed for a very long time. Whether he would feel guilty later on was neither here nor there. This had nothing to do with Marion. And he had no need to feel guilty about Janet, who, with her legs round his neck, was clearly enjoying herself.

It was quite a time before they got round to conversation. Jeremy began. 'What a nice flat you've got.'

'Not bad. Jermyn Street suits my needs.'

'Do you have a country house as well?' asked Jeremy.

'I did. But I loathed country life and my husband was quite happy to buy me this when we divorced. You did better than I did, didn't you? You're a happily married man. I take it you married for love?' As Jeremy was silent, she got out of bed and went to the kitchen to make a pot of tea. Jeremy noticed that, although Janet must be, by now, nearer forty than thirty, she could still look good walking upright and naked, a very unusual feat. Her hair flopping over her cheeks, she poured tea. 'Come along, now. It's surely time you got back to your wife and children.'

'I haven't any children. My wife hasn't been able to have them.'

'I'm sorry. Oh dear, that's what you left me for, wasn't it? The right children by the right wife.'

'Have you? Got children, I mean?'

Any anxiety Jeremy might have felt about the long-ago abortion he had forced upon Janet was dispelled by her answer. Clearly, it had done no permanent damage. 'Two. A boy and a girl. They spend most of the time in the country, with my ex-husband. It's better for them. I'm not a particularly good mother. Though I must say, we do have a lot of fun, when they come up to stay with me. Rupert's very good about that. Well, actually, he's only too glad that I do half-terms and a chunk of the holidays. And they love taxis, and restaurants. They never want to go to the zoo. They get enough of animal life, in the country.'

46

From then on, Jeremy had fallen into the way of going to see the always receptive Janet whenever he felt like it. Now, he sat at his own dinner table, looking with satisfaction at his guests. Having produced good wines to complement his wife's excellent food, he hoped the evening would go on for a long time yet. 'Peter,' he said, 'nice to see you again. How's the job going?' He could never quite remember what Peter's job was, but it was the question he always produced.

'All right,' said Peter.

'And the young lady we met, at Laura and John's party? How is she?'

'Fine,' said Peter, bracing himself in the knowledge that more communication was expected of him than just one word. 'We're thinking of getting married, actually.'

'Splendid. Good news. It ought to call for champagne, but we'll let that wait until you bring her down. Where is she?'

'She's gone up north, to see her mother and father.'

'Up *north*?' said Veronica, in an outdoor privy tone of voice.

Peter looked at his father, to whom, in spite of an hour together in the pub, he had been unable to convey his news. He could not make himself look at his mother.

'Will you be playing cricket tomorrow, Peter? Jeremy is, and you are, too, aren't you John?' Marion interposed.

'No,' said Peter, 'I'm no good at games, especially cricket. I remember at school, the master saying "Keep your eye on the ball, Fenby," and all I could say was "Where *is* the ball?"' Peter was the only one of Laura's children who had had to have glasses as a child.

'Come and watch, then. Keep me company.'

When it was time for the guests to go home, Jeremy decided to walk back with them. 'Let me give you an arm, Veronica,' he said. Veronica accepted with alacrity the gallantry she considered her due. So, by the time he returned, Marion had stacked the dishwasher and gone to bed, which was what he hoped would have happened. He watched late

TV until he was pretty sure she would be asleep.

On Sunday morning, Laura awoke with a desperate desire for a few hours' privacy. She dreaded the morning. Trying not to snap at John, despising herself for being bullied, not knowing why Peter had said nothing about his impending marriage to her, all seemed utterly unbearable, and unfaceable.

In order to get this time to herself, she lied. 'I have a dreadful headache,' she said. John, believing her, wanted to bring aspirins and tea. 'No,' she snapped. 'Just leave me alone.'

Peter, coming home after the dinner party, had been unable to say more about Deirdre. And, as neither John nor Laura would press him, even Veronica dared not. The window of his boyhood bedroom wide open, he breathed in the drifting garden scents whose familiarity he had never defined. Syringa, roses and tobacco flower; he was at peace, for this while.

Sunday cricket always began at two o'clock, in the long-lost tradition of morning church. Peter strolled over to the pitch on the green, with his father. 'Will you come, Mum?' he asked.

'Later.'

Jeremy, in flannels and his well-laundered shirt, was already there. After about twenty minutes, Peter saw Marion approaching. 'How nice,' she said. 'Can I come and sit with you?' She liked the look of Peter, this afternoon, better than last night. He was wearing old corduroys and a sweater, which suited his gangling stoop better than the grey suit he had worn at dinner. The suit was good enough, by no means cheap, but it seemed to have been chosen without pleasure. He gave her his deckchair and sat on the ground, looking up.

'Thank you for having us all, last night,' he said.

'Oh well, it gave Laura a break.' Then she said, abruptly, 'I got the opinion you hadn't told her that you are getting married. Isn't that rather odd?'

'I suppose it is. I find it difficult to tell them things.'

'But surely! Something as important as that?'

'Oh, I don't know. She's got enough to worry about, with my grandmother in the house.'

'But why should you getting married be a worry? Deirdre's very pretty, and you love her.'

'Mmm. Were you in love when you got married?'

'Very much so. I think I'd been in love with Jeremy from the time I was eleven years old, when my mother died and he was kind to me.'

'Are you still in love?'

'It's different, after all this time; hard to explain. But, believe me, falling in love at the beginning is what it's all about. And now, Jeremy and I are so interwoven we can cope with what comes. It's been rotten for him, that I couldn't give him children.' Peter could hardly believe what he was hearing, when she added, 'He's got a mistress.'

'How do you know? Has he told you?'

'Of course not. I just know. Peter, if you're not in love, don't get married.' She put out a hand and gently stroked Peter's head in a motherly way. 'I wish I had a son like you,' she said.

Peter burst out laughing and his whole face was transformed. 'I'm a bit old for that job. You'd have to have given birth when you were about three.'

'Ten, to be precise. Come on, let's stroll over and have a closer look at the cricket. Pull me up.' Peter jumped to his feet and pulled her up out of the deckchair.

6

Jeremy was batting, and looking extremely handsome. 'It's no wonder,' said Peter, 'you fell in love with him.' He suppressed a pang of fury when he thought of Jeremy's getting away, unchallenged and unblamed, with taking a mistress when he had so sweet a wife. Sweet, and generous.

'Oh look,' said Marion, 'there's your mother.'

Laura had assuaged the guilt induced by her morning hideaway, by insisting that yes, of course she wanted Mummy to come with her to watch the cricket. Actually, she really did. Life with her mother was a lot easier when other people were around. Veronica was rapidly provided with a seat by a young cricket-wife who knew her place.

'What train have you got to catch?' Marion asked Peter.

'I hadn't thought.'

'Better go for the four o'clock. It's not a good idea to chance anything later, on a Sunday. I'll take you to the station, if you like.'

'That's awfully kind. Are you sure it isn't putting you out?'

'Not in the least. I've watched Jeremy bat, so I've done my duty. He likes me to watch him bat.' She went over to Laura. 'Laura, I've had enough cricket for the afternoon. Will you let me drive Peter to the train?'

Peter, in the passenger seat of her car, was much lighter and leggier than Jeremy. Not that Jeremy was all that often in her car, other than when they had been out and Marion, like all good Swanmere wives, did the driving. Peter, folding in his long, thin legs, leaned away from her, towards his door. He was silent, but glanced at her and smiled. His bony nose had a bump where his spectacles rested.

They arrived ten minutes early for the train. 'Don't wait,' said Peter.

'I'm in no hurry,' said Marion. They walked slowly up and down the platform. 'Deirdre will be pleased to have you back.'

She wondered if he had not heard her. To her surprise, he merely said, rather suddenly, 'How is your lovely garden? I haven't seen it for ages.'

'Jeremy has improved the patio, he's put up a trellis for climbing roses. And he's got some more urns, beauties, actually.'

'That's not the garden I meant. I meant *your* garden.'

'Oh, my jungle! As jungly as ever.'

'That's the part I mean. I loved it when I was a kid. We all did. I can remember the feel of the cedar needles. I loved stroking them.'

'You did. I remember that, too.'

'And it smelt lovely. There was a red rose.'

'You must bring Deirdre over, next time you come down,' said Marion, privately deciding that Jeremy's part of the garden would be much more Deirdre's scene than hers. She couldn't imagine Deirdre in her wild garden, and didn't want to.

The train came in. Peter tripped over his bag. Between them, they bundled it and him into the carriage. Marion slammed the door and Peter put his head out of the window. Marion lifted up her face, turning sideways to be kissed on the cheek. The train gave a little jolt. Neither of them knew exactly how it was that Peter's face came down. The kiss, a proper kiss, surprised both of them.

As the train moved away, Peter hung out of the window, watching Marion. She was waving, growing smaller and smaller, until she was at last out of sight.

The train stopped at every opportunity, and every station. For Peter, the slow journey was exactly what he needed, for he had a lot to think about. He remembered every word Marion had said to him, most of all, 'Peter, if you're not in love, don't get married.' It was having been in love in the first place that explained Marion's ability to weather Jeremy's infidelity. Jeremy was indeed a lucky man.

For the first time, as the train chugged slowly along, bringing him nearer and nearer to Deirdre, Peter made himself face facts. He was not in love with Deirdre.

He was grateful to her. She had rescued him from a deadly dull existence and, more than that, she had made him extremely comfortable in her flat. And, although he paid his full share of the expenses, he was well aware of living in a charming apartment he himself could never have afforded to buy.

Yes, Deirdre had been more than kind to him. Furthermore, he was aware of her background. Although he had never met her family, he could imagine what an ordeal it must be for her, on the occasions when she went home, to have to turn up not only unmarried but also living in sin.

Even so, he resolved that it would be wrong to marry her on those grounds alone. And as unfair to her as to himself. Of course he wasn't going to walk straight into the flat and say 'Hallo, Deirdre, I've got news for you. I'm not in love with you and I'm not going to marry you.' What he would do would be to suggest they postpone the wedding for, say, a year. In that time, Deirdre would surely find someone else who would do just as well as he, and probably better.

As it was her flat, the obvious thing for him to do was to get out of it and leave her free to make a new start. Now he followed up this decision with another. He would leave his job. That way, the 'postponement' would become a permanency, and Deirdre would be able to believe that she had broken their engagement off, simply because of his irrational behaviour. He felt clearer in his mind, happier than he had been for months. And deeply grateful to Marion Clark, who had set his mind in the direction of sanity.

Deirdre, arriving back at the flat, found Peter rather quiet. But then, he often was. He was drinking a cup of tea as she entered. 'Would you like some?' he asked. 'It's fresh, I've only just made it.'

'No thank you, dear.' Her sisters addressed their husbands as 'dear', as though they were already middle-aged. It was the term used by married women, and Deirdre now adopted it. 'I've got a load of stuff to bring up from the taxi,' she continued. 'Give me a hand, will you, and then we can have a drink later, and go and have dinner somewhere. Goodness knows, I've eaten enough at Mum's. But there was nothing to eat on the train, Sunday, you know, so I'll want something later.'

It took quite a while for both of them to unpack Deirdre's cases. 'This was my grandmother's,' she said, taking a large tablecloth of fine Irish linen, inset with Limerick lace, out of tissue paper.

'It's beautiful,' said Peter.

'Yes, it is, isn't it? It's a family heirloom, one my grandmother made. My sisters have one each, but mine's nicer than theirs. They're only passed on to married daughters, but Mum let me have mine now, since we're to be married so soon and they won't be coming down for the wedding. Dad's not very well.'

'I'm sorry to hear that. Nothing serious, I hope?'

'I'm afraid it is. The doctors won't say, but I'm afraid it's the big C. He rallied a lot while I was up there, wanted to know all about you. He said you sounded a great chap, even though you're a southerner. He's bluff, my dad. "I thought you'd never get married," he said, "you're that picky." So I told him yes, I am, and he'll be glad of it when he meets you.'

In spite of himself, Peter couldn't help but be touched by the thought of an old man who was willing to lose his daughter to a southerner, for the sake of her happiness. He felt badly that he was about to dash these hopes, but dash them he must. The thing to do was to get out of the flat, away from the shared bed. 'Let's go and have dinner. You must be starving.'

Peter wasn't quite sure whether a full or an empty restaurant would be best. The matter was decided for him by Deirdre's choice of Jackie's, the current in-place, especially on Sunday nights. There was no table-hopping at Jackie's: none was necessary, as its whole point was its one long table, round which everyone was crowded. Intimate friends, sometimes of as long as a week's standing, bellowed their latest news to each other, up and down and across it. And tonight was Deirdre's night.

Above the crunch of crudités, she happily told her news. 'The wedding's in July. Here in London, rather quietly. My father is seriously ill, and my mother looks after him, so they won't be able to come. We'll have Peter's family, of course, though I wouldn't dream of letting his mother do any of the arrangements. Bless her, she's got enough on her hands, looking after *her* mother. She's a wonderful person. We would have liked to be married in church but under the circumstances, we both think a register office is appropriate. Don't we, darling?'

'I had bridesmaids, at my first wedding,' said a thirty-year-old divorcee.

'I don't really believe in all that,' said Deirdre. 'It didn't make your marriage stick, did it?' She had had a few wines by now. 'In any case, my own sisters are married, so they're out, and Peter's sisters are too old.'

'You're not that young yourself,' said the divorcee.

Deirdre smiled, and took Peter's hand. 'Quite true,' she said sweetly. 'That's why *we* know what we're doing, isn't it, darling?'

Peter refilled his glass, and found he had lost the power of speech. He could only suppose that Deirdre had got him back to the flat, for he remembered no more until he woke in the early hours of the morning, to find he was being made love to. Even fuddled as he was, his body responded to the pressure of her warm thighs. Sheer sexual need drove him. He vaguely hoped he was pleasing Deirdre, although he couldn't manage to kiss her. Afterwards, he slept as she left the bed and went to take a shower.

In later years, Peter looked back with amazement at this time of his life. In the ensuing days, marriage plans went forward as inexorably as a rising tide. There was just no turning back. Peter had, in fact, inherited from his father a sense of right and wrong. Wrong was to betray. Right was to marry the girl.

Suddenly, there were wedding present lists at Peter Jones and General Trading.

The wedding was booked for mid-July. Deirdre attended to sending out the invitations. She bought a blue costume, and a hat. She even bought her own wedding ring. While she was at it, she bought one for Peter to wear, as well. She was going to be a married woman, and all the world would know it. She used her credit card, happy in the knowledge that it would very soon become a joint card, part of being called Mrs.

The reception was held at the flat. Ten municipal minutes had confirmed for Peter that he was now a married man. Luke, who had jollily nipped into the flat before the ceremony, in order to assure himself that the champagne was drinkable, was best man. Ann couldn't come. Saturday was the busiest, at her restaurant. But she had made a cake and had it delivered to the flat, ready for the reception. Judy managed to get time off, and pleased Deirdre by having dressed elegantly for the occasion. John Fenby, who had never in his life attended a wedding in a register office, and was rather surprised by its brevity, wore the only morning suit to be seen.

Laura had taken some trouble about what to wear. She did

so want to please Deirdre, so she went to Swanmere's one dress-shop, where the clothes were more expensive than in London. 'Are you the mother of the bride?' asked the proprietress.

'No. It's my son.'

'Ah, the mother of the groom. Take my advice. Wear beige. It'll help you to keep your mouth shut.'

The beige outfit was actually very pretty, and John Fenby was, as ever, proud of his wife.

Marion had not come to the wedding. She had contributed generously to the wedding-present list, with a set of china which she hoped would please Deirdre. Jeremy made it to the reception, stayed until the end and made a point of saying to Laura, 'I've got to go back to the office. Got a load of stuff to catch up on. I'll have to stop in town for the night. Such a bore. Would you be a dear, and give Marion a ring when you get home? Tell her I'll be back as soon as I can. It's so hard to talk, in the office.'

'Oh,' said Laura, wondering why Jeremy was making such a point of telling her this.

It was time to go. The bride changed her blue costume for a tan one. The groom took off his dark suit and put on the pale cream lightweight Deirdre had made him buy. The honeymoon was to be spent in Venice. Peter admitted to himself that the cream suit was really rather a nice one.

Laura got home to find Veronica in plaintive mood. She'd got it wrong again; Veronica's protest that she was far too old to stand up for hours at wedding receptions was, of course, supposed to have been overridden. She rang Marion.

An ironic chuckle greeted the news that Jeremy wasn't coming home. 'Working late?'

'That's what he said.'

'Did the wedding go off well?'

'It was fine. Deirdre looked very nice.'

'In blue?'

'Really, Marion! Yes, it was blue. But it was a good shade, and it suited her. With that blue-black hair, you know.'

'I wonder how soon she'll have to start dyeing it,' said Marion. 'Now. Why don't you ask your mother if she'd like to come to lunch with me tomorrow.' Laura could have kissed her.

Venice in July was too hot for Deirdre. Fortunately, it was cool in the shops. Peter found himself surprisingly happy. While Deirdre bargained over glass and necklaces, he wandered about the mystifying lanes. He, too, liked the shops for the very reason that so many of those that Deirdre discovered were hidden away in the very part of Venice he was discovering.

Now that she was a married woman, Deirdre no longer assumed the bestriding position she had adopted, for the first and last time, on that fateful night after dinner at Jackie's. The missionary position was only proper, and it was usually too hot for that.

Peter gave in to languor, and a new-found enjoyment of the beautiful city. 'Do you know,' he said early one morning, 'I'd like to live in Venice. It would be wonderful to live here for ever.'

'That's really sweet of you. But it's just because it's our honeymoon, believe me. When we get back, we'll have to think about moving. The flat will sell well. I thought we might think about buying a house in Bromley.'

'Why Bromley?'

'It's on the right side of London, and only thirty miles from Swanmere. I know you like going to your parents'. And there's a good train line. You could get to your office just as quickly as you've been doing from my flat. And we could manage for a while with only one car. I could take you to and from the station.'

Peter wondered why Deirdre's reasoning sounded so like his grandmother's.

★

It was not the moment for Peter to mention his wish to leave his job. It didn't seem to matter any more. And Bromley *was* within an easy drive of Swanmere. It was nice of Deirdre to consider his parents. And he had good friends, there. Well, one.

7

On the first day of August, Mr Bagshot rang loudly and confidently on Mrs Clark's front door bell. Marion, who was at the further end of her garden, did not hear the bell. Mr Bagshot rang again. Her car was in the drive, so she must be there. Returning at last to the house, Marion found him waiting.

Her new bathroom still had no tiles. 'Mr Bagshot,' she said. 'What brings you here?'

'Your bathroom. Had a little trouble, getting the right tiles.'

Forbearing to comment that the 'little trouble' in question had taken three months to resolve, Marion merely said, 'So you've got them now, have you?' She was well aware that Mr Bagshot had deserted her bathroom for the sole purpose of latching on to a couple who had recently arrived from Hong Kong, with a great deal of money. She also knew that the house they had bought in Swanmere had not, after all, suited them, so they had promptly put it on the market and departed. However, once again she kept her temper. She was sick of the sight of bare cement on the walls in the bathroom. 'Very well, then. You'd better get started. I take it you have today in mind?' Mr Bagshot had.

She got out the dust-sheets and spread them all over every vulnerable surface. Then, there being nothing more she could do, she returned to her garden.

The cherry tree's leaves were darkening. Its blossom was long gone. Red-hot pokers, faithful friends, were all about.

Poor things: the bluetits ate all their flowers, but they went on producing more. And the roses went on, too. Marion never sprayed them. She let the greenfly have their share, fattening up to become, in their turn, dinner for the ladybirds.

Sitting and swaying gently on the old swing, she thought about Peter. Her strongly held belief that his marriage was a mistake was one she kept to herself. Her only indulgence was to allow herself a slight giggle when Luke made one of his more outrageous observations on his new sister-in-law, 'Deirdre of Peter's sorrows'. She normally enjoyed chatting with Laura about 'the children' as Laura still called them, but this was now out of the question.

She was rigidly determined not to stir up any anxiety in Laura. For Laura, she knew, had managed to convince herself that her daughter-in-law was a dear girl and a good wife.

Now, pushing on the ground with her foot to send the swing a little higher, it was as though Peter, a serious twelve-year-old, was watching her and stroking the green, fronded needles of the cedar tree. The odd thing about Peter had been that, though he was uncoordinated indoors – if anyone was going to drop anything or fall over anything, it always seemed to be Peter – he was never clumsy in the garden. Filled as it was with trailers to trip on, unexpected branches to bump into, he always made his way round it without mishap. He had never even trodden on an insect. The image faded. Peter was no longer a boy, but a married man. The wisest course was to adopt Laura's method. After all, what use was truth, in the face of a *fait accompli*?

From Peter, Marion's thoughts turned to herself. Which naturally led on to Jeremy.

She was fully certain that Jeremy had no idea that she knew he had a mistress. That he had not told her was neither surprising nor particularly painful. It did not even come into the category of deception. It had simply always been Jeremy's way to protect her from unpleasant realities. She knew him so well! 'I should do,' she said aloud. 'He's the only man I've ever known. I must be unique. Maybe I ought to be in the *Guinness Book of Records*: the woman who was a virgin when she married, and faithful for twenty years.'

She got off the swing, and wandered over to the cherry tree. As she leaned against its comforting trunk, a ladybird landed on her hand. 'Ladybird, ladybird, fly away home. Your house is on fire, and your children are gone.' It was the maid, Hetty, holding her hand on one of the many days when her mother had been asleep, who had taught her the ladybird rhyme.

She smiled as she thought about her awareness of Jeremy's mistress. Her detection was the classic banality. A scent on his neck which was none she had ever used, a tiny flake of nail polish in the middle of his back, and, of all comical things, a crumb of flaky pastry trapped where one didn't normally expect to find the remnants of a *mille-feuille*.

For some strange reason, she did not feel jealous. Maybe another entry for the *Guinness Book of Records*, the un-jealous wife! She wasn't jealous but she was curious.

Just as a child growing up in an ordinary semi-detached house might ask herself what it must be like to live in Buckingham Palace, Marion wondered what it must be like to be a mistress. Silk sheets, maybe? A wine-rack in the bathroom? Painted nipples? In some ways, she wished she could ask Jeremy about it. Did a mistress take the initiative in love-making? Evidently, they served French pastries in bed, their cholesterol level being, presumably, no part of each other's responsibilities.

Facts brought her down to earth with a bang. Oh Lord, Veronica was coming to lunch. Thank goodness she'd got a home-made consommé in the freezer, and some smoked trout. She rushed into the house, tripped over the rucked-up dust-sheets and set the dining-room table.

'I really take my hat off to you, Marion,' said Veronica.

'Builders in the house, but you still do everything just as nicely as usual.' She spread the butter, which was patted in a nice little dish, lavishly on the French bread Marion had hastily defrosted and heated in the oven.

'How nice of you. Mr Bagshot turned up this morning, to finish my bathroom. At last.' The normality, the everyday mundanity, of having Veronica over as usual, had wrenched her quite away from her garden, and from fantasy.

'So Peter's married, then,' said Veronica. 'I have a feeling that Laura doesn't really like Deirdre.'

'Oh? Has she said so?'

'Of course not. Laura says very little, to me.'

'Do you like her? Deirdre, I mean,' asked Marion, practised at avoiding Veronica's perpetual criticisms of Laura.

'What little I know of her. I wasn't at the wedding. You weren't either, were you?'

Marion had been asked, but had not wished to go. Veronica's presence had been, she knew, skilfully avoided. 'I didn't want to go to London. Jeremy went, and that was enough for both of us.'

'Before I leave, you must let me see how Bagshot is getting on in your bathroom.'

Marion was only too pleased to oblige. And serve Mr Bagshot right!

She gave Veronica tea and tomato sandwiches. Cucumber, she knew, was not agreeable to Veronica's digestion. At last, she gave her an arm to walk across to the Grange. She could not help but admire the old woman's refusal to use a walking stick.

Before entering the house that she had so ruthlessly made her own, Veronica paused. 'You asked,' she said, 'if I like Deirdre.'

'And do you?'

'She has nice manners. At least, she certainly has with me. And she takes trouble over her appearance, which is as it should be, when a woman marries a businessman. Yes, I like her.'

8

'Well, I never,' said Ann to Len, reading her morning post in bed. 'Old Jude wants to bring us some clients.'

Judy and Ann Fenby had spent their childhood being mistaken for twins. They looked alike and were generally thought to be alike. Ann, the sturdier of the two, had reached the same height as Judy, early on, which added to the confusion. Only they knew how different from one another they really were.

It had taken them years to get over the mutual resentment that this bracketing had engendered. But now that, at last, they had grown up and gone their separate ways, they found that the very difference between them was what had allowed them to become friends.

'Clients?' said Len. 'I didn't know she had clients.'

'Well, she has. That's Swanmere for you. Just because she works in an office, everyone thinks she's a secretary. Well, she isn't. She's an account executive, and that's not just another name. She says, "Dear Ann, I've got to entertain some clients from Japan. They are very important to me, and I hope you can help."'

'Japanese,' said Len. 'Good, I can do something interesting with vegetables.' Len was not only *chef de legumes*, he was also a dedicated vegetable eater. He had no objection to meat, but he was getting bored with the usual clientele, who came all the way up the River Thames to eat dinner in this charming island restaurant, then looked through the menu, discussed new dishes as though they were really going to order them,

63

but settled for steak or, if they were in a daring mood, duck.

The lunch (for midday had been decided upon as the right time for this business exercise) went off well. Judy, whose talent for organisation had got her where she was today, had arranged that her guests should be taken to play a round of golf on a very expensive, large and well-watered course. She also made a good impression on them by being womanly and sending them off with Charles, the company chauffeur, a decent man who knew when to stay quiet and when to step in, and who had the added value of looking like a stage ambassador. From Judy, he only needed a nod and a wink.

This left Judy free to stay on for the afternoon. 'Can you get out for a bit and come for a walk? I could do with a breath of air. And I'm free until Charles comes back for me.'

'My grand sister,' said Ann, as they crossed the little bridge that joined the island to the bank. 'It's long grass, here. What about those posh shoes?'

'I'll take them off,' said Judy. It always took them a while, when they hadn't seen each other for some time, to get going.

They strolled for a while, pulling feathery heads off grasses. 'Is that a cuckoo?' asked Judy.

'Of course not, silly. In Aug*ust*, away he must. That was a pigeon.'

'Have you been home lately?'

'No. Granny doesn't approve of Len and me living in sin, as she puts it. And I haven't seen Mummy for quite a while, either, since we couldn't get to Pete's wedding. I was sorry about that, but Saturday is one of our busiest days.'

'Your cake was a big success, though, Annie. I know, because I ate a bit of it. It was delicious.'

'Well, at least you managed to get there.'

'I made a point of it. I wondered why Pete married her, and now I think I know.'

'Oh? And why?'

'Well, he's a bit like Daddy in some ways. Don't look so

64

surprised! I know he doesn't look like him and he certainly hasn't inherited his sporting talents. But he's got Dad's old-fashioned notions of how a gentleman should behave. And not only had he been living with her, but also in *her* flat. It's quite simple, really. He thought it was the right thing to do. And, who knows, it may work out.'

'Maybe you're right. D'you like her?' asked Ann.

'I don't find her very interesting, but what's that got to do with it? As long as she makes Pete happy, it's none of my business. In any case, I wouldn't call myself a good judge. I don't think I know much about people, unless they are people I'm working with.'

'Have you been home lately, yourself?'

'Not lately. I've been so busy. It takes me all of Saturday to write up my reports. And I'm so tired by Sunday that I just stay in bed.'

'Alone?'

'Alas, yes.'

'What about that chap, Gordon? Wasn't that his name? I liked him. Aren't you still going out with him?'

'No.' Judy didn't want to talk about the recent end of her affair with Gordon. She remembered his angry voice: 'I can't believe even you would do this. Have you any idea how difficult it is to get tickets for Glyndebourne? And you calmly tell me, on the day, that you can't come because you've got to take some bloody client out. Well, forget it. I'll find someone else.'

'For Glyndebourne?'

'For good.' So that was that. 'About Mummy,' Judy continued. 'I'll make a real effort to get down there. I saw Luke the other day. Do you know, even he hasn't been home for weeks?'

'Goodness! I wouldn't have thought even Granny could faze Luke.'

'She doesn't. But he says he can't keep his mouth shut with her. And it makes it worse for Mummy, and you know how

Luke adores Mummy. I tried telling him all old people get difficult. I must say, he made me laugh. He just said "Bollocks. Granny's always been a self-centred, destructive bitch." And you know, Ann, our little brother's pretty smart for his age. He says senility is only like being drunk. It peels off the veneer and exposes what the person is really like.'

'There you are!' Neither of them had heard Len coming up behind them. He kissed Judy on both cheeks. 'Was your lunch all right?'

'If you'd seen the plates coming out, you'd have known it was all right, and more. Your vegetables were inspired. I didn't even recognise some of the things, but my guests were amazed. The Japanese have a curious sort of politeness. They bow and smile but they don't often commit themselves to praise. But one of them told me it was the first meal he'd really enjoyed in England.'

Len was off on his subject. 'I used samphire, you see. And then of course I grow all the herbs myself. I put just the flowers of the sage with the onion, and then tarragon on its own. I deep-fried it. I'm afraid the bill is going to be a bit on the high side.'

'No matter,' said Judy, 'it was well worth it. Thank you, Len.' She kept quiet about the expense account over which she had control. She knew that Ann and Len, although they ate well and had free accommodation, were paid peanuts. They owned nothing, and hadn't a credit card between them. A good thing they loved their work!

'Do you know,' said Len, 'when I was coming up behind you, I could hardly tell the difference between you. You've got exactly the same legs. Very nice legs, too, I might add.'

'Would you love me if I had fat legs?' asked Ann.

'Well, I would if they got fat now. But I mightn't have got to know you in the first place. I'm a leg man, me.' He put an arm round Ann, and tousled her curly hair. Ann's hair, which was always stuffed under a white cap for work, got no more attention than a daily wash and an occasional chop with the kitchen scissors. Judy's, equally fair, was perfectly groomed and its curliness resolutely smoothed out.

Ann and Len went back for the evening preparations. Judy was driven away by Charles; she sat between two Japanese who kept a suitable space between themselves and her.

Having promised Ann that she would get down to Swanmere, Judy decided she must do so. She had not seen her parents since Peter and Deirdre's wedding day.

She arrived on Saturday morning. Veronica was out of the door first. 'Hallo, Granny,' said Judy, kissing the powdery cheek. 'How are you?'

'Not very well, I'm afraid. But I never complain.'

Judy had brought a briefcase of work she hoped to attend to over the weekend, but she left it in the car and went in search of her mother. Having hugged her, she sat at the kitchen table drinking coffee while Laura prepared lunch. It was obvious to Judy that Mummy, who never failed to produce dinner for Daddy in the evening, was now preparing two main meals every day. Under cover of slicing the runner beans which were to be for dinner, later, she studied her mother's face. She hadn't aged, it wasn't that. And she didn't look bad-tempered; far from it. No, what was wrong with Laura's pretty face was that it bore clear signs of unremitting self-control.

'I've got some duty-frees for you in the car. I was in Paris the day before yesterday and I got them on the way back.'

'Oh darling, how thoughtful. And you don't smoke yourself. How lovely of you not to be disapproving.'

'Will Daddy be in for lunch?'

'No, he's playing golf. He plays a lot of golf, these days.'

Lunch was served on a small walnut table, in a sunny little room at the back of the house. Judy remembered that it had once been Mummy's own domain, full of books and the silk smocked party dresses she had always failed to finish making, and then had to rush out to a shop called Babydom, in the nick of time for whoever's birthday it was. The room now seemed to be Granny's property. Daddy played a lot of golf these days! She could hardly blame him.

'And how is your career, Judy?' asked Veronica. 'All you girls have careers. In my day, a girl might take a job until she married. I was lucky, I didn't have to. I married young. I know things are different now but, even so, surely it is odd for a reasonably attractive girl to be thirty and still not married.'

'I'm not quite twenty-eight, Granny.'

'There's plenty of time,' said Laura. 'You've no need to make a grandmother of me yet.'

'I,' said Veronica, effectively killing that conversation, 'was a *young* grandmother.'

Judy went out to the car, brought in the cigarettes, collected an ashtray and a box of matches and put the whole down in front of her mother. 'Thank you, darling,' said Laura, determinedly lighting up.

'I'll clear away,' said Veronica. Judy remained glued to her seat as her grandmother carried out one plate, holding it as though its weight was about to cripple her.

'Does she have a rest, after lunch?' asked Judy.

'No. But I'll sneak off for an hour, if you don't mind.' The hour after lunch was Laura's only remnant of privacy.

'Mummy, this is ridiculous.'

'No darling, it's just sad for her. I put myself in her position. I'd hate to have to give up my own home. I ought to try harder to find things to interest her, things for her to do.'

Once she had seen her mother go upstairs, Judy tiptoed past the drawing room, where Veronica was sitting upright, *Daily Telegraph* on lap, spider-bright eyes at the ready for a passing fly.

Having escaped the web, what to do next? Judy was too exhausted to get her briefcase and do the work that waited in it. She wandered away, reflecting that if she was worn out after three hours of Granny, what must it be like for her mother?

She walked to the village green, with the lovely pond she had fished Ann out of so often, when they were little. Summer sun had coated its surface with duckweed, through which two swans swam, wearing green stoles round their white breasts. Her feet took her over to Marion's house.

Jeremy answered the door. 'Hallo, Judy, how nice to see you.'

'There's no cricket today, then?' She knew perfectly well there wasn't; she had just crossed the empty village green.

'No. That's tomorrow. I'm watching a bit of sport, actually. Marion's down in the garden, why don't you go and find her?' He was already back in front of the TV set as Judy went out through the french windows.

Marion, hearing someone approaching, hastily reached for her shirt and pulled it on. Fortunately, it was long enough to conceal the total nakedness in which she had been soaking up the August sun.

Judy sat down quietly. It had always been easy to be quiet with Marion, whose orderly house she had so admired, as a child. She pulled a clover flower and chewed on its sweet taste. 'My mother's a saint,' she said, at last.

'I know,' said Marion. 'But there's not a thing I can do about it.'

'At least I made her smoke, in front of Granny. Granny had to clear the lunch dishes, as a protest. Well, one dish!' She changed the subject. 'It's funny how different your garden has always been from your house.'

'That's what your brother said.'

'Luke?'

'No, Peter.'

'Did he? I always feel I don't know much about Peter. Luke's easy. And I saw Ann not long since. She and Len put on a terrific lunch for some clients of mine.'

'Tell me about your job,' said Marion. 'It sounds so

69

exciting. You said you took your clients to Ann's restaurant. I just think you are incredible.'

'Granny doesn't. She thinks I'm a complete flop because I'm not married.'

'Don't let that worry you. Her generation sees things differently. People don't marry so young, these days. Have you got a boyfriend?'

'I did have. But he left me because I was too busy to go to Glyndebourne with him, when he'd gone to a lot of trouble to get the tickets.' She changed the subject. 'I've come down here because I'm worried about Mummy. But I don't know if I'm any help at all.'

'You are. Just being there helps.'

'Do you really think so?'

'I do. And I gather Peter's coming down quite soon. That will help, too.'

'With Deirdre?'

'Well, of course with Deirdre. Your grandmother likes Deirdre; well, she approves of her. I must say that Deirdre is courteous to her, so Laura may get a little break.' Marion found herself getting into realms she should avoid, though whether about Veronica or about Deirdre, she was not certain. 'I'd better go and make some tea for Jeremy. I gave him Welsh rabbit for lunch, with a glass of beer. Time I woke him up for a cup of tea.'

'What are you giving him for dinner?'

'Chops and vegetables. It's what he likes.'

'I think Mummy's got lamb for Daddy, for tonight. She loves him, you know. And you love Jeremy.'

'Yes. Come in with me and have some tea.'

'Thank you. And Marion, I also want to thank you for helping Mummy out, having Granny over so often, the way you do.'

'Oh, my dear, why shouldn't I? I'm extremely fond of Laura and, in any case, what else have I got to do?'

Judy said nothing. The pleasure of escaping, long ago, to

the niceness of Marion's house, from the chaos of the Grange and her little sister and brother, had been one thing. Growing up had brought her the knowledge that something was sadly missing in the life of the woman who had always been so kind to them all.

9

Peter and Deirdre paid their first post-marriage visit to Swanmere at the beginning of September. It fitted in with Deirdre's wish to look at a house in Bromley.

'Is there any point, when we haven't yet sold the flat?' asked Peter.

'We've got to start somewhere. Get our eye in.'

To Peter, the house they had just seen was utterly depressing. His heart sank, as Deirdre praised every room and every appointment, from the knicker-pink bathroom suite, the white and gold fitted cupboards, to the built-in barbecue and scrolled ironwork that made a 'feature' of the poky patio.

He could hardly believe his ears when, in the car, she fastened her seat-belt and announced, 'Well, we can forget that one. It is quite out of the question.'

'But they thought you liked it. Goodness, *I* thought you liked it. You let them think we wanted to buy it.'

'I was only being polite. And the patio was quite nice, I thought. But it's over-looked on either side. It wouldn't do at all.'

Peter certainly hadn't liked the house, though he hadn't noticed that it was over-looked. But although he was relieved, he was obliged to say 'I'm afraid we aren't going to get anything better at the price. And, let's face it, we're never going to get what we're asking for the flat.' It was nice of Peter to say 'we' since the price had been firmly fixed by Deirdre.

'Then we'll just have to stay there until we do. It's a good thing I didn't come off the pill. I know you want children, darling, but it makes sense to wait a while, don't you agree?' Peter couldn't recollect having said anything, so far, about children, or even having thought about them. Being unable to think of anything to say, he merely nodded.

They arrived at the Grange only just in time for lunch. There was no chance of a pre-prandial drink, as it was more than anyone's life was worth to keep Veronica waiting for her food. However John, who was aware that he and Laura hadn't seen much of their children lately, made up for that by putting three bottles of his best wine on the table.

In the end, lunch went off unexpectedly well. Veronica, with her unsurpassed talent for divisiveness, decided to woo Deirdre. 'Well, my dear, I see you warrant the best wine. We don't usually have anything like this at luncheon. No, thank you, John, none for me. Well, just half a glass then. I must toast the bride.'

Deirdre, who prided herself on knowing what was what, sat with her glass untouched until after the toast had been drunk. She would also leave her napkin crumpled on the table, in spite of the fact that Laura, John and Peter all folded theirs in readiness for the next gastronomic onslaught. Veronica, as usual, dropped hers on the floor. Meanwhile, Deirdre turned to her and said, 'We looked at a house on the way down.'

'And did you like it?'

'I'm afraid not. It had simply no privacy.'

Veronica, who knew Deirdre's origins perfectly well, nodded agreement. 'Goodness me, no, that would never do. Maybe you should think of moving further out. I'm sure prices are much lower, here in Swanmere.'

'It's rather a long way for Peter to travel to work every day,' murmured Laura, putting cheese on the table.

'Is there no pudding?' asked Veronica, wincing away from the Brie as though it smelt, which it deliciously did.

'I've got a pudding for tonight,' said Laura.

After lunch, Deirdre escorted Veronica for a stroll round the garden. 'Laura,' said Veronica, 'always seems to need a rest after lunch. I can't think why. I never do.'

'Neither do I. I'm afraid I'm one of those people who always have to be doing something.'

'Laura reads a lot,' said Veronica, in an indulgent voice.

'I just never have the time, I'm afraid. I like to be sure Peter comes home and finds everything nice. And then, of course, there's this business of getting a house, I have to see to all that. Do you find time to read, Mrs Chadwick?'

'Yes, I do. But please call me Veronica. Yes, I find reading a great comfort. I'm alone a great deal, you see. Not that I complain, an old woman like me has to come to terms with being alone. But books are my friends. Not novels. I never read novels. What I like is a good biography. So true, biography. And one so often runs across people one has known.'

Peter and his father lingered over the lunch table. 'We may as well finish this,' said John, pouring the remains of the red wine. 'It's pleasant, with cheese. Glad to see you, my boy.'

'It's good to be here,' said Peter. It was a toss-up which of them found it harder to think of something to say. John had never been able to recognise certain likenesses to himself in his first-born. For a start, John had always been athletic. And the very first time he had thrown a ball to Peter, aged four, the child had stood still, closed his eyes and cupped his hands in the vain hope that the ball would fall into them. John had tried patiently – he was neither hasty nor a bully – to teach Peter the rudiments of ball-games. But not only was Peter quite unable to grasp the idea, but he also, however much he wished to please his father, found it impossible to understand or be interested in any sports at all. There was never any question of John and Peter Fenby refusing to talk to one another. It was simply that they had nothing to talk about.

Eventually John wandered off and Peter cleared everything away and stacked and started the dishwasher.

The afternoon, though slow, passed quite well. Deirdre,

who was getting on splendidly with Veronica, insisted on getting the tea. Laura, although sick of the sight of food, normally hated people helping her in the kitchen: it was so much more trouble than it was worth. But on this occasion, Peter was here to show Deirdre where the cups and the cake tin lived, and Laura was able to take comfort in observing the apparent intimacy of the two of them, side by side in the kitchen.

By bedtime, Deirdre was in a friendly mood. In her satisfactory situation, a married woman who had just shown her ability to fit in with her in-laws, particularly her grandmother-in-law, she was quite willing to let Peter make love to her.

Peter tried, and failed. Deirdre didn't mind. There wasn't much point in it, anyway, until they were in a position to start a baby.

Although he really had not comprehended the exhaustion Laura was suffering since her mother's arrival, John, who loved his wife, was aware that she needed, as he put it, 'cheering up'. And his idea of cheering her up, not a bad one as it turned out, was to make love to her. In bed, he put his arms round her and kissed her. For John Fenby, the rules of masculine morality were simple, narrow and straightforward. The idea of husbands whose wives, at fifty-plus, should be replaced by a newer model, was repugnant and, above all, *wrong*. As a result, although Laura bore, as every woman must, the scars and droops of child-bearing and of ageing, these stigmata were, quite simply, invisible to him.

Laura didn't feel in the least like making love, and hadn't, for a long time. She just thought she was getting too old, since she would never have admitted that having her mother in the house thoroughly inhibited her. Now, she gave in, at first simply from kindness to John. But suddenly, an unexpected result came about. John was a wordless lover. Laura was astonished when his silent stroking and his still athletic legs suddenly, overwhelmingly, swept her into

75

passion. 'Phew,' she said, afterwards, 'it's a jolly good thing I'm past child-bearing age.' She then slept better than she had done for weeks.

Peter slept fitfully. Shortly after five o'clock, he gave up trying and got out of bed. Deirdre didn't stir. Her well-cut, blue-black hair was neat on the pillow. The night moisturiser had sunk into the pale skin of her face, leaving only a faint trace on the pillowcase.

Dawn was just beginning to make itself felt as Peter quietly opened the front door of the Grange, and went out. At the flat, you couldn't get out without switching off the burglar alarm. But John and Laura Fenby, like most people in Swanmere, refused to believe that such things were necessary. The front door wasn't even locked.

He wandered over to the village green. The quiet swans swayed sleepily on the pond. A frog, browsing on the edge, sensed a footstep and dived in with a great plop. In a few hours the green would be full of cricketers, his father and Jeremy Clark among them.

Leaving the green, without thinking where he was going, Peter found himself pushing along a narrow footpath. A sweet scent came his way. His long legs lifted him over a low wooden gate. He knew where he was. He was in Marion Clark's garden.

He stood quite still, listening to a soft rustling sound.

'Peter!' There, close enough to touch, stood Marion. 'Peter,' she said again.

'How did you know it was me?'

'I just knew.'

'It might have been an intruder. Yet you came straight on. That's not very wise.'

'What brought you here?' asked Marion.

'I couldn't sleep.'

'Neither could I. I always come out here when I can't sleep.'

'I smelt a delicious scent.'

'Probably meadowsweet.' She leaned against the trunk of the old cherry tree and stretched her arms up above her head. Peter, a foot taller than Marion, took her hands in his and put them on his shoulders. She let them stay there. It was so comfortable, resting her arms this way while his arms wrapped themselves round her.

He lifted her away from the tree. 'I don't like that dressing gown. It's a hideous colour, on you.'

'It was mail-order,' said Marion, smiling.

'But not male-order. Pun.' Peter was rather pleased with his little joke, particularly since Marion took its point and laughed as he removed the dressing gown. 'You have very small breasts,' he said, as Marion very gently led his hands to hold them.

He stood very still. He knew without a doubt that he was experiencing the greatest moment of his life. Marion made no protest as he gently pulled her down on to the grass. She had not felt so happy for a long time. Peter's love-making was glorious.

For Peter's part, he felt a surge of confident joy in his own power to please. He knew by instinct just where Marion would like to be touched. Then, momentarily sated, he propped himself on one elbow and looked. He looked and looked at every bit of her, in a way he had never done with Deirdre, or any woman. There was a tiny track of hair, like a soft arrow, leading up her stomach. He picked up her hands and noticed her fingernails, perfect ovals, except one. 'You've broken a nail,' he said.

'I did it grating cheese. Fancy you noticing, and you haven't even got your glasses on.'

'So I haven't.' His glasses were entangled in a bramble.

'It's a good thing we didn't roll into that,' said Marion. 'We would have been full of prickles.'

Peter was kissing the little arrow. He raised his head to say, 'Are you happy?'

'Very.'

'I'm in love with you, Marion.'

Marion knew she should feel guilty. But she felt no such thing, she was simply absorbed in this one delightful moment, being made to feel young and beautiful. She stroked his floppy hair. Just when she most wanted him to, he made love to her again.

'Oh look, the sun has risen,' she said later.

'I know,' said Peter, looking at her as the morning rays shone through the fuchsias, glowing rosily on her body. 'You look about sixteen,' he said.

'It's Sunday morning, isn't it?' said Marion.

'I suppose it is. Why do you ask?'

'I always give Jeremy bacon and eggs and fried bread, on Sunday mornings. He works it off, playing cricket, so it isn't all that bad for him.' It was the first time she had mentioned her husband. Peter had not thought of Deirdre at all.

The sun was now high in the sky.

Peter watched Marion, her dressing gown now tightly belted, walk up through the garden. He realised he was still naked. He put on his clothes and made his way back to the Grange.

Everyone was at breakfast. 'Oh, there you are,' said Deirdre. 'I wondered where you'd got to.' Peter kissed his mother and then remembered to kiss his wife. He found himself with a good appetite for breakfast, and absolutely not one shred of guilt or shame.

Laura, happier herself after the night, thought that Peter looked well rested. She had come down in her dressing gown. That Deirdre had appeared, properly dressed in what looked like a church–going suit, was a sign of her good manners. All would be well, surely.

'There seems to be no All-Bran,' said Veronica, who had elected, on this occasion, to come downstairs for breakfast.

'No,' said Laura, 'there isn't any. I forgot to get it. Have some toast.'

10

Jeremy Clark woke up on Sunday morning, alone in bed. This neither surprised nor worried him; Marion often got up early and left him to sleep in, on a Sunday morning.

Although he often spent nights in town during the week, Jeremy usually came home on Friday evening or, if not then, early Saturday morning. Their weekends were always the same. Saturday night was always dinner-party night, either given or taken. The Clarks' dinner parties were much the grandest, it being the understood thing that the childless couple were better able to spend money than those who were putting their children through school and university. Jeremy didn't mind this in the least, even though he knew quite well that by no means everyone in Swanmere, however upper class they might be, paid for their children's education. He was a generous host and enjoyed entertaining on a lavish scale.

Jeremy, this morning, was slightly hung-over. This was no thanks to his hosts. Marion, who did a day a week at Oxfam, had accepted an invitation from a fellow worker, a pale woman with an anxious face. Jeremy had a vague idea they were vegetarians. If they weren't, their food could certainly be blamed for tasting like it, and he strongly suspected their wine of being non-alcoholic. As a result, he had needed rather a lot of brandy when he got home.

On this lovely September morning, he knew exactly where Marion would be. There would be plenty of time to be outdoors later, at cricket. He felt no need to get out of a warm bed and go dabbling in the dew. But if Marion chose to wander out into the garden at an ungodly hour, and get wet feet, he could see no reason why she shouldn't.

The sun was getting well up into the sky when Jeremy, having a comfortable scratch and looking out of the bedroom window, saw his wife emerging from her jungle. He opened the window and called out, 'Good morning, darling. Have you been having a nice time out there?'

He watched, as Marion raised her hand in a small wave, and then made her way slowly across the lawn until she disappeared, on her way into the house. He went to the head of the stairs, and called down, 'Where are you?'

'I'm in the kitchen. Do you want a sausage with your bacon and egg?'

'Yes, please. And some mushrooms and fried bread.' Jeremy always made the most of his treat of Sunday breakfast. All week, Marion kept a firm hand on his cholesterol, but on Sundays she allowed a fry-up *and* real butter. 'But come up here first and get out of your wet slippers, and I should think your dressing gown must be soaking, trailing it through the wet grass.'

'It's all right, I've got some dry slippers down here.'

The smell of bacon and coffee brought Jeremy downstairs. Marion was sipping coffee. 'Aren't you having any of this?' asked Jeremy, as he did every Sunday morning, in spite of the fact that Marion never had more than coffee and fruit for breakfast.

Now she stood up, took her coffee cup to the sink, and left the room saying, 'I'll go up and get dressed while you're having your breakfast.'

'Aren't you going to sit and talk to me?'

'I'll be down in a while. Anyway, you know you'd rather read the paper, it's the one day you get the time.' The Sunday paper was already on the table, placed there by Marion.

During the morning, Jeremy did things on the patio while Marion did things in the house. Then they went to lunch at the Beaters' Arms. They did this at least once a month: it was Jeremy's way of showing Marion his appreciation, by saving her the preparation of at least one meal.

They were face to face at a table for two. Marion seemed to be rather silent. They often ate in silence; well, a lot of married people did that. But now, for various reasons, Jeremy bestirred himself to be sociable. 'I like that dress you're wearing. It's a good colour for you. You look very pretty.' He then realised that he had just spoken the truth; Marion was, indeed, looking very pretty today. She was inclined to be too pale, even a little drawn sometimes. But today her cheeks were quite pink. She looked, somehow, softer.

After lunch, they went straight over to the cricket field. The Swanmere side won the toss, and went in to bat. While he was waiting for his turn to go in, Jeremy sat beside Marion. Laura and her mother joined them and Marion, he noticed with approval, engaged Veronica in conversation, while Jeremy talked to Laura. 'Oh,' said Laura, 'there are Peter and Deirdre.' She beckoned. Deirdre came straight over and placed herself between Marion and Veronica, taking charge of the conversation. Marion now sat in silence.

Peter, after a brief glance in their direction, walked round to the other side of the pitch. Funny fellow, thought Jeremy, you'd almost think he was avoiding us. Still, he always was a bit gauche. A few desultory hand-claps told him that he was now in to bat.

Working off his lunch, he batted away like a blacksmith, scoring boundaries, and smiling at Marion when she applauded them.

At the end of the game, everyone adjourned, as usual, to the pub. Mild surprise was caused when Jeremy announced, 'I won't come, if you don't mind. I've got things to do.'

'What is it, motor-racing on *Grandstand*?' asked someone. Jeremy just smiled.

What Jeremy wanted, and had been wanting ever since

lunchtime, was to make love to his wife. As soon as they were inside the front door, he put his arms round her and kissed her. 'I startled you,' he said, as his kiss missed its aim, almost as though she was evading it. Let that be a lesson to me, he thought, I haven't done much courting of her, lately.

He followed her into the sitting room, where she was standing in front of the television set, holding the *Radio Times* in her hand. He came up behind her, leaned his head down on hers, put his arms round to where his hands could grasp her small hip-bones and gently propel her backwards and on to the sofa.

'Oh, Jeremy. You'll tear my dress. And do be careful of the sofa, it's a new cover.'

'I'm sorry, darling, I won't tear your dress.' He knew her so well. He knew how fussy she was about the state of her house and its furnishings. But he also knew, after all he always had known, the passion that was in her, the passion he had uncovered when she was still little more than a girl. And he wanted that, so desperately it was hard to restrain himself. But he did it.

She was quiet in his arms as he carried her upstairs. She couldn't escape, and she knew it. But Jeremy was gentle in victory. He stroked and petted her as though she was a kitten.

Marion was almost drowsy by the time the touch, the touch she had first welcomed so long ago, had its effect. Perhaps because she had already been so astonishingly awakened earlier, her body, in spite of her mind, leapt into life under Jeremy's skilled love-making.

Afterwards, Jeremy rested on his elbow, looking down at her, his faithful little wife. Poor little one, she had suffered so over being unable to have children. She deserved every kindness from him, and she should have it. Her ardour just proved how much she needed to be made love to. Even so, he had more sense than to make any spurious promises to himself, sentimental as he felt at the moment, about his extra-marital activities.

Laura Fenby awoke on Monday morning, making resolutions. As every day now felt like a year, most mornings began with the equivalent of New Year's resolutions. This time, she decided that the only way to get along with her mother was to entertain as often as possible. To that end, she invited the Vicar and his wife to come to dinner later in the week. They accepted. They always accepted.

She took trouble in preparing her mother's breakfast tray. Then she took a deep breath, carried the tray upstairs and knocked on the bedroom door. Veronica was sitting up, managing to convey that she had been awake for hours. 'Good morning, Mummy. I hope you slept well.'

'I got a little sleep, yes, thank you.'

Laura watched as her mother picked at the toast, butter, marmalade, sliced banana to give potassium, milky coffee with sugar, and marvelled. She wondered if, should she live to grow old, she would inherit this talent for not apparently eating anything and yet leaving the tray as though locusts had been at it. 'The Carews are coming to dinner on Wednesday,' she said.

'The Vicar and his wife.' Veronica pushed her tray away, so that the marmalade spoon fell off and landed on the eiderdown. 'Suitable company for your ancient mother.' As this was pretty much the exact truth, Laura said nothing and took away the breakfast tray. She could sponge the eiderdown later.

On Wednesday afternoon, Veronica unerringly entered the kitchen as Laura was stuffing garlic into the lamb. 'I won't be able to eat *that*,' she said.

'You always eat it, and I always put garlic in it.'

'There's no need to bite my head off. Really, Laura, you're so snappy these days. Anyone would think you were in the menopause instead of well past it.' Laura decided it was better to say nothing, and to be seen as sulking rather than snappy. She looked at the kitchen clock, thinking, 'Roll on drinks time.'

Later, having her brief hide-out in her room, Laura took herself by surprise by actually falling asleep, with the result that she was hurrying to get the dinner preparations finished as the Carews rang the doorbell. John was not yet home, so she showed them into the drawing room, where Veronica was already seated, poured drinks and excused herself. Hastily roasting almonds to throw on the pudding, she had at least the satisfaction of knowing that, in the role of hostess, her mother would have a happy half-hour, and, in fairness, would do it well.

She was right. Dorothy Carew, who had heard on the village gossip-circuit that Laura Fenby was having a tough time of it with her old mother, decided that everyone must have got it wrong. She was a charitable woman, anyway, but no one, listening to Veronica, could have seen her as anything but a charming old lady. 'And how is Jennifer?' she enquired. 'Such an attractive girl.' Having flattered Jennifer's parents sufficiently, she went on, 'Peter was down at the weekend, with his wife. She's done wonders for him, he's improved beyond recognition. He's quite come out of himself.'

Laura could hear the murmur of voices, so that was all right. Nevertheless, she popped in to make sure everyone's glass was filled. 'Oh good, I see Mummy's looking after you,' she said.

As she returned to the kitchen, she heard her mother's tinkling voice, saying, 'Really, my daughter! Don't be surprised if she even comes to the table in that terrible apron. When I had a home of my own, I wouldn't have dreamt of entertaining without changing at least an hour before my guests arrived.'

Shutting the kitchen door, Laura did not hear Dorothy Carew's gentle comment: 'Perhaps you had a cook, Mrs Chadwick.'

John, who had got home as quickly as he could, made straight for the kitchen. His effort to kiss his wife was thwarted by lips so tightly compressed as to be untouchable. 'Why haven't you got a drink?' he asked. 'They were all on seconds, by the look of it, when I came past the drawing room.'

'I haven't had time,' said Laura.

'I'll get you something.'

'Better not. I'm too tired. I'll have a glass of wine at dinner, if I ever get it on the table.'

John grabbed her shoulders and made her look at him. 'Now, listen. You listen to me. You need a holiday, and I mean it. And I mean soon. How about Brittany? Or Madrid? Or Greece? Anywhere you like.'

'Oh, John, for God's sake don't be ridiculous. How can I go on holiday? I can't see me ever going on holiday again.'

'Your mother could go into Mulberry Lodge for a couple of weeks.'

'You know that's out of the question. I've sharpened the carving knife for you.' It struck neither of them as strange that John, who wouldn't have had the faintest idea how to cook a joint of meat, always carved.

Laura gave no further thought to the suggestion of a holiday.

A few days later Laura, completely surprised, found herself being bustled through Gatwick Airport. She was unused to crowds, and was quite frightened when she saw the jostling queues at every desk, people behaving as though they would never get on their planes unless they crashed their trolleys into the legs of those in front of them. She felt dizzy, and almost wished she could faint and get out of the whole trip, which had been so hastily thrust upon her.

John took her elbow and led her away from it all and through a door labelled THE CAPTAIN'S DECK. Within, she could hardly drag her feet through the carpet, which seemed to be at least four inches deep. 'John,' she at last managed to say. 'This is the first-class lounge.'

'It certainly is. I've got us first-class tickets.'

'You must be mad!'

'Is that all the thanks I get?' said John, smiling with satisfaction.

'Oh darling, and you don't even like going on holiday.'

'All the more reason to do it in comfort.'

Laura, in a daze, fell into a deep chair and found a glass of champagne put into her hand. After that, further champagne on the plane successfully anaesthetised, for the time being, her anxieties about leaving her mother.

All she could remember was that Luke, frivolous Luke whom she loved best of all, had swept in and taken over.

'Now, Dad, I tell you what you do,' said Luke, who quite agreed with Dad that Mum had to have a break. 'You give me a bit of money and I'm on for a fortnight.'

'What about your job?'

'Easy-peasy. I can pick it up any time. Seventy pounds a week, say a hundred and fifty for two weeks, money off for the second week, and you've got me.'

'A hundred and fifty is money off? Don't you mean a hundred and thirty?'

'No, Dad. The penalty clause would have made it two hundred.'

'Is a cheque all right?'

'I'd rather have cash.'

In the end, John Fenby parted with not only the hundred and fifty but an additional twenty pounds, 'for shopping'. Shopping, he knew full well, would turn up on the grocer's bill later.

'Don't forget to look in the freezer,' said Laura. 'I've left you some different pâtés, there's salmon, there's chicken liver and a couple of others. They'll do for lunches, and I've made quiche. It's not Granny's favourite but it's easy for you to do. Just heat it a bit. And –'

'Don't fuss, Mum. Anyway, I can cook.'

'And you will wake up in time to give her her breakfast in bed?'

'Of course I will. I'll set the alarm.' Luke beamed with pride at having thought of such a responsible idea. Unfortunately, thinking of it was as far as it went, so that, on his first morning of Granny-sitting, he met her in the kitchen at ten o'clock, with a 'You're very lucky I haven't had a heart attack' expression on her face. 'Hi, Gran. I thought you always had breakfast in bed. I was just going to get it,' he said cheerfully.

'I have breakfast at eight o'clock. I eat so little that I become faint if I don't have breakfast on time.'

'Oh well, sorry about that. How about a fry-up, now you're here?'

'Just some toast and a banana. I'll do it.' Veronica tottered

87

about, as Luke fried sausages and bread and added baked beans. Poor Veronica; for once her appetite really was impaired. She turned away from the noxious fumes of Luke's repast.

'Now then, what do you want to do today? I'll take you out.' After protests that she wasn't up to it, Luke managed to persuade his grandmother into the car. As they jounced around the country lanes, she seemed a little more contented. He remembered how Mum, when he was little, would put him in the pushchair and joggle him along for miles until he nodded off. The only difference was that Granny never seemed to nod off.

Veronica, in fact, was thoroughly enjoying herself. 'This is quite a treat, darling,' she said. 'I hardly ever get out.'

'You go over to Marion's quite often,' said Luke firmly.

'Oh yes, but it's such a pleasant change to be taken for a drive.' Veronica was about to complain that Laura never took her anywhere, but common sense stopped her. Her comfort for the next two weeks was dependent on Luke. And Luke loved his mother.

Luke enjoyed driving; Granny enjoyed being driven. But, after a couple of days, even easygoing Luke felt the need of a break.

Little realising that he was following his mother's escape route, he got out alone on the pretext of shopping, and went down to Marion's house for a bit of sanity.

'Hallo, Luke. You're supposed to be doing the shopping, I take it.'

'How did you know?'

'I just did. Looking after Veronica's not as easy as you thought, is it? Still, you're kind to do it. Just stick it out and keep your end up. You'll find that pays, with your grandmother. She's a bully.'

'I know. But I don't let her bully me. She's all right, as long as you stand up to her. In fact she likes it better that way. And she's quite fun in some ways. She's certainly got energy.'

'Indeed she has. Would you like some coffee?'

'I'd love some, but I'd better not stay too long.'

'I wouldn't worry. She'll probably give you a hard time when you get back, anyway.'

'She won't. I won't let her. Even so, I am supposed to be looking after her. Do I take it you don't like my revered grandmother very much?'

'On the contrary, I do quite like her. But then I'm not family, so I get the charming side, you see. Actually, she can be very amusing company at times, as you have found out. I hear all about the grand old days of double-damask dinner-napkins and parlour-maids. I do worry about Laura, though.'

'So do I. I love my old mum.'

'If only we could persuade her that your grandmother would be perfectly happy in that residential place. You know, Mulberry Lodge.'

'Oh God, don't say that to Mum. The very thought would make her die of guilt.'

'Yes. Veronica's a great guilt-inducer.'

'She doesn't make me feel guilty,' said Luke.

'Well of course not. Guilt is not a thing you suffer from. But your mother does, heaven only knows why. She also happens to be a naturally loving woman. She loves John, she loves you lot, she doesn't know how not to love your grandmother. Veronica, on the other hand, doesn't love anybody; I don't think she ever has. And she likes to have everything about her tidy, which is something that doesn't matter two hoots to Laura. That's why Veronica likes coming here, I'm so boringly meticulous. She'd be a lot happier in a place where she's waited on and meals are on time, and the corridors are alive to the sound of a vacuum cleaner. Have another biscuit.'

'You're an amazing woman, Marion. It's no wonder we all love you. Talking of all of us, have you seen old Pete since he married Dreary?'

Marion swallowed coffee. 'Yes, he did pop in once. He

seems very well. And you shouldn't call Deirdre "Dreary".'
This was said automatically, as a matter of form.

'Well, sooner Pete than me. If it *was* me, I'd soon be
looking elsewhere. But I don't suppose such a thing would
occur to Pete. He's the faithful type.'

Marion carried the coffee cups over to the sink. When her
face had cooled, she turned to Luke and said, 'Why don't you
bring your grandmother over to lunch tomorrow? She likes
to come and you can get away for a few hours.'

'You're an angel, Marion.' If only you knew, thought
Marion. Luckily, Luke went on, 'Do you still have that rope
swing you put up for us when we were little? I'd love a go on
it.'

She went with him down to her wilderness. He was far too
large for the old swing. He must weigh at least a stone more
than Peter, and she hoped the swing wouldn't break under
him. She hadn't been this far down the garden since what she
could only think of as 'that morning'. Her body took her by
surprise, as a shudder suddenly rocked through every muscle
from thigh to shoulder. It was a sensation of pure bliss.
Getting herself under control with difficulty, she hastily called
out to Luke, 'What shopping were you going to get? Have
you made a list?'

'A list? Should I?'

'It's the usual way. Never mind, come back in and I'll find
you some eggs and things. We'll put them in a grocery bag
and your grandmother won't know the difference.'

'You devious woman,' said Luke. How true, thought
Marion, throwing in, for good measure, a bunch of grapes
and some apricots she had intended to use in a health-giving
fruit salad for Jeremy.

Luke went cheerfully home with his loot. 'You got grapes,
I see,' said Veronica. 'How thoughtful. I need fruit, and
grapes are quite easy for me to digest.'

'Marion thought they would be good for you,' said Luke,
honestly.

'Have you seen her, then?'

'I popped in.'

'You should have taken me.'

'I will, tomorrow, if you like,' said Luke.

Veronica was perfectly content with this arrangement. Marion had indeed been right: not only was Luke a stranger to guilt, but his grandmother quite accepted him as he was. She saw herself as a reasonable and considerate woman. She really had no idea that she had almost driven Luke to distraction, and would have been hurt and astonished to be told so. That she couldn't help being destructive was a fact unknown to her.

12

'Having a wonderful time. I hadn't seen Cannes since our honeymoon. A lot of it looks the same, except the *girls*! Everyone's topless, except us old things. Daddy keeps saying "well, *really*!" – whatever that may mean. Hope all well at home, love, Mummy and Daddy.'

Peter and Deirdre were having breakfast when Laura's postcard arrived. 'I hope your father doesn't have a heart attack,' said Deirdre.

'I think I ought to go down to Swanmere for the weekend,' said Peter. 'Poor old Luke's been looking after Granny for a week now and it's only fair I should give a hand.'

'Of course we'll go,' said Deirdre.

'Do you want to? I don't mind going alone.'

'Don't be silly. It would look very odd if I didn't come; your grandmother would be most surprised. And heaven knows what state things are in, with only Luke.' Deirdre very much liked the idea of a couple of days at the Grange. She and Peter were still no nearer finding a place she considered fit for them to live in. The Grange, although crying out for new curtains and chair-covers, not to mention redecorating, was a lovely house, the sort of home Deirdre longed for.

'Pete and Dreary are coming down for the weekend,' said Luke to Marion.

Marion nodded. She had been thinking about Jeremy when Luke made his announcement.

Jeremy had a mistress; she had a lover. There was nothing wrong in that. But Jeremy had hardly spent a night in town, lately. She didn't mind him being around. What worried her was that he didn't seem very happy. Jeremy had always been the ebullient one. She realised that she had depended upon his confidence, as opposed to her own lack in that department, a lack that had been assuaged only by her almost obsessive attention to the elegance and orderliness of their house. But now, there was an air about him that worried her. She wondered if things had gone wrong in the City. She would have liked to tell him that it didn't matter if they were broke. But you didn't say things like that to Jeremy Clark. In thinking about Jeremy she had, for the moment, almost forgotten the uninhibited pleasure she had had with Peter in the garden.

'Would you be an angel, darling Marion? May I bring them over to dinner on Saturday night?'

'Of course.'

'Thank you, you're a darling. And you know Granny loves coming to you for a bit of gracious living.'

'Would you like me to ask Jennifer Carew? She's a nice girl your sort of age.'

'If you're match-making, forget it. I've years to go before I'll be marriage material, if ever. In any case, Jennifer Carew wouldn't touch me with a barge-pole. Well, would you, if you were a vicar's daughter and had brains in your head, which she has? Jennifer's going to marry money, and good luck to her. I'll be happy to partner Granny. As far as my love-life is concerned, I've got a gorgeous bird in London. Legs up to *here* and a yummy job in advertising. She's married and divorced.'

'She must be a lot older than you, then?'

'Not all that much. She married young. She's twenty-three, and I'm old for my age, aren't I?'

Marion shook her head. Incorrigible Luke, he had the gift of always making one laugh, whatever worries might be in the background. 'Let's say 7.30 on Saturday,' she said.

If Marion had hoped that a conventional evening, with two wives and their two husbands, would erase what had happened between her and Peter, she was mistaken. She and Peter went through every device that manners could contrive. Peter was attentive to Jeremy. She was charming to Deirdre.

Deirdre responded by effusively praising the cold watercress soup. 'You must give me the recipe,' she said.

Marion, who always cooked by the book, was able to oblige. When she came to 'half a pint of double cream, preferably Jersey', Deirdre laid down her spoon and ate no more. As Marion moved to take away the soup bowls, Luke, seeing Deirdre's, snatched it cheerfully. 'You are a chump, Deirdre. Don't take it away, Marion darling. I'll slurp it while you clear. Funny thing,' he said, naughtily to Deirdre, 'Marion can eat anything and never put on an ounce. Oh well, I suppose genes differ.'

Marion gave him a sharp look. She could not understand why Luke, by nature as kind and bouncing as a big puppy, was nasty not only *about* Deirdre but also *to* her. She brought in the salmon. Jeremy did his duty with the wines and dinner rumbled on.

Afterwards Deirdre put Luke in his place by taking his grandmother over. She announced that Veronica was tired. A slight tussle ensued. Veronica was, in fact, very tired. But she clung on as long as she could. At last she said, 'I'm not in the least tired, but I expect you young people have had enough of me. Amid much demurring, she allowed Deirdre to get her coat. There was half an hour's fuss in the hall about who should do what. In the end it was decided that Deirdre should take Veronica home, assisted by Jeremy. Luke snatched the opportunity to get down to the Beaters' Arms for a quick one before closing time. Peter, unnoticed by anyone except Marion, quietly cleared the table and joined her in the kitchen.

He kissed her. 'Oh Marion, I long to make love.'

'So do I, Peter.' Marion had no intention of saying any such thing, but the words just slipped out.

'But not here. Where can we go? I don't want to hurry, I want to lie quietly with you. But soon.'

'If I can find a way, shall I telephone you?' She hoped she meant to do no such thing.

'Yes, please.' Peter took and held her hand. It would have been quite a different story if he had groped or pawed.

It was all so easy. 'Jeremy,' said Marion. 'There's an old friend I want to see. Quite a way away, so I'll have to stay overnight. Is that all right with you?'

Jeremy had a lot on his mind. In fact, he could hardly look at Marion without feeling guilty, and guilt was a new and very uncomfortable experience. 'Of course. Anyone I know?'

'Sort of.'

'Well, you do as you like.'

'There's a casserole in the freezer.'

A telephone call later, and Marion and Peter were together.

Marion giggled. She couldn't help it. 'Do you think they'll notice there are two cars out there in the car park?'

'There's no "they" in motorway motels. I've brought some champagne. And some caviare.'

'Oh Peter, you are ridiculous. I am ridiculous. We are both ridiculous. Making love in a motel. Is it dark yet, or is it just those curtains? They're double-lined – they must be used to the likes of us.'

'There is no "likes of us" in the whole world. And I told you, motorway motels don't have "theys".'

'You are beautiful, Peter.'

'I am not. I am skinny and muscle-less.'

'Don't fish.' She ran her fingers down his ribs. Gently pushing him away, she got out of bed.

'Where are you going?' asked Peter.

'To look for that caviare. You've made me hungry.'

'All right, but don't be long about it. I miss you already.'

'There you are, sir,' said Marion, bringing the caviare and champagne, plus saucers from the Teasmade and tumblers from the bathroom.

Peter spread the caviare on crackers. 'Dear, dear, I forgot a lemon. Should I run across to the shop and get one?'

'Don't you dare. Careful with that champagne. It's such a waste to spill it where you are spilling it.'

'Aren't you lucky I'm not a racing driver? It would be all over the ceiling instead of where it is now.'

'Peter,' said Marion, seriously. 'What are we doing?'

'Hadn't you noticed? We're making love.'

'But I'm ten years older than you and I'm barren.' She deliberately used the ugly word. 'Don't you find it odd to be in bed with a woman who can't have children, a woman with something missing?'

'What a cruel and wicked way to speak of yourself. "Something missing." I have never held in my arms anyone so whole and perfect as you. I relish the insides of your elbows, and the skin on your back. And your bottom is like two peeled hard-boiled eggs.'

'I hope you like hard-boiled eggs,' said Marion.

'Only these ones. Quail's eggs, I think. As to children, I suppose I'll have to provide children in due course. But with you, I'm having love. And I'll tell you what I mean. When I'm inside you, I feel possessive. I feel I'm finding my way around in my own little home, and there's no one but me in there, and no little intruder to come into it.' He rolled over, in joyous conceit. 'Now, tell about me!'

'Oh, you! Well, you're all right, I suppose. You rest lightly on me. I like your hands. You make me flutter and I like the way you talk. This can't go on, you know. But it doesn't matter. I suppose this is a sort of capsule. When you're a grandfather, I'll be dead.'

'Would you marry me, if we both got divorces?'

'Certainly not. Marriage is quite another matter. Marriage is like my house and this is like my garden. So shut up and love me.'

There was no question of making this first motel room 'our place'. For Marion, it was the irresponsible affair she had never had, that rare thing between a man and a woman, bodily enjoyment for its own sake. She believed it was the same for Peter. That he had mentioned marriage was just bed-talk. All Marion knew about sex, so far, was what she had learned from Jeremy, and what he had told her about the behaviour of other men.

'You know,' said Marion, on their third or fourth occasion together, 'you could really call us platonic.'

'I beg your pardon?' It was, by now, November; cold, dreary and dank outside the warm bed in the warm little room. 'You didn't have a classical education, then.'

'I didn't have any education at all. But I know what I mean.'

'Oh, very well. As long as this is what you mean, I'll go along with it.'

'What is love? 'Tis not hereafter; present mirth hath present laughter,' suddenly sang Marion, in a soft, true voice.

'I didn't know you could sing,' said Peter. 'But then, I suppose I don't know anything much about you, outside of us.' They had never, so far, spoken to each other of Deirdre or Jeremy. But now Peter went on to say, 'Does Jeremy ever wonder where you go?'

'I wondered that, too, at first. He's been very different, for the last few months. He always expected me to be where I should be, on the dot, even if I didn't know when or if he was coming home. I didn't mind, I took it for granted. After all, he's given me a lovely home and a more than comfortable life, he has his rights. Even the right to have his mistress.'

'And you put up with it?'

'Yes. He didn't tell me; he wouldn't. He's fond of me, and protective, in his way. But I've known, for ages.'

'You really are a remarkable woman.'

'No. I'm just a woman who couldn't give her husband children. He wanted children and it was a great disappointment for him. He was faithful to me for a long time, when we were trying to have a baby. In fact, if I'd managed to have one, he would have become a father and a faithful family man. But he likes women, so I don't blame him. He wanted a son and then a little girl.'

'You love him, don't you?'

'Yes. There's love, and love, you know.'

'Not for me. I never knew what love was, until you. It wasn't just that morning in the garden. I'd been falling in love with you for a long time.'

Marion knew she should put a stop to this now. Peter should have her as a mistress, just as Jeremy had his. But somehow she found it impossible to explain, impossible even to speak, with Peter's mouth covering her own, completely. Anyway, if what Jeremy had taught her about men was true, and she had no reason to believe otherwise, this passion for her on Peter's part would pass. In the long run, the Peter she knew was too loyal by nature to leave his wife.

There was no more talking. Peter was making love with a passion that rocked them both.

There was to be a big family gathering for Christmas, at the Grange. Laura, her holiday long behind her, had settled back into the routine of keeping Veronica happy. With no time to herself, she simply blessed her good fortune in having a houseful of sons and daughters to come. 'Won't it be too much for you?' asked John.

'No. It would be a lot worse without them.' She even contemplated an afternoon with a book, since Ann and Len had announced that the restaurant was closed over Christmas, and Len had a new way of cooking the sprouts, with almonds.

And Ann had already made pudding, cake and mince pies. The food would be delicious, which would please Veronica. She determined that Ann and Len should share a bedroom, bravely telling herself that it was her house and she could decide. And Deirdre got on well with Veronica. And they would have Marion and Jeremy over for Boxing Day, which would be nice, since Marion seemed to get on so well with Peter.

In yet another obscure and faceless motel room, Peter and Marion were in bed on December the 14th. Peter kissed Marion's shoulder and said, with pride, 'You know these tiny tits of yours? They've got bigger. Quite round, and there's a darling little blue vein running down each side. Do you think me making love to you did that?'

It had.

13

About this time, Jeremy's mistress, Janet, found herself in a surprising situation. Never having been in love in her life, she now discovered that she was getting really rather fond of him. This took her aback, as the nearest she had ever come to a feeling of affection was a cool liking for her children, which she would have been the first to admit would not have come about had they not been nice looking and bright.

'You know, Jeremy,' she said one afternoon as she gave him a cup of tea and his favourite chocolate biscuits. 'It may surprise you, but I've been thinking about you.'

'Have you? How nice!' said Jeremy.

Janet could see he liked the flattery but, even so, a slight clattering of the teacup indicated what might be a certain anxiety. 'Don't worry. I'm not thinking of marriage, or anything silly like that. It's just that I feel I owe it to you to tell you about something. It's not a nice thing. I was young and greedy at the time, and I wanted you to marry me.'

Jeremy, getting back to his tea and biscuits, said benevolently, since all that was safely in the past, 'There could have been worse ideas. We would have had a child, and I have to say I'm sad that Marion hasn't been able to have children. A child of yours would have been lovely.'

'Yes. My kids are nice. But Jeremy, that time I told you I was pregnant, I wasn't. I needed money. I knew you weren't going to marry me, you were going to marry Marion, she was right for you and I was wrong. She was your housemaster's daughter and I was a common little girl from nowhere. Being with you showed me a glimpse of the life I wanted to have. So I got money out of you, to begin to get it. Do you understand? There wasn't an abortion. I didn't even miss a day. At the time, I just thought it served you right to have to pay up. But now, now that I know you better, I sort of want to clear my conscience.'

Jeremy put down his teacup with care. 'Well,' he said, 'I'm glad the money came in handy.' The biscuits, melt-in-the-mouth *langues de chats au chocolat*, rested on a solid silver filigree bonbonnière, so valuable as to be opulent. The teapot and milk jug were silver. The napery was fine linen, hand-laundered at one of the many expensive establishments which were Janet's daily privilege.

Janet's highly efficient domestic help was always out of the way when Jeremy came, so she pushed the tea-trolley out of the room with her own hands. Her hands were delightful, soft, slim and manicured. 'Bed?' she invited, laying one of them on Jeremy's brow.

'Not just now. Thanks all the same. I've got to get back to the office, actually. I want to talk to Tokyo before closing time.'

'See you soon, then, darling,' said Janet. She had only meant to right a wrong. She had no idea of the devastation her unprecedented attack of conscience would cause.

Hours later, Jeremy did get back to the office. First, he walked. He walked from Jermyn Street through to Piccadilly. From Piccadilly he walked to Hyde Park Corner. From Hyde Park Corner, he walked down Knightsbridge and then along Sloane Street. Then, for a long time, he stood in the King's Road outside the narrow door that had once, years ago, led the way up to the little flat in which he and Marion had begun their married life.

He remembered the old woman doctor he had taken Marion to. She was long dead; she must have been nearer seventy than sixty even then. Anyway, even if she were still alive, Jeremy was not a man to go to a female doctor. His firm had a doctor, a good doctor, used to the likes of Jeremy and his colleagues. He checked their hearts, counted their cigarettes, suggested regimes for winy bellies and sympathised with unfortunate illnesses contracted by busy men who had to find their pleasures where they could. He made an appointment.

'My dear chap, you're forty-five. Your wife is almost forty. Why do you want to find this out? What does it matter? No children? I can think of worse things!'

'I want to know. I have to know. Has it been my fault, all this time?'

'Oh dear, I wish people wouldn't say "fault". Oh very well, then, if nothing else will satisfy you, I'll put you on to the right chap.'

The assessment of Jeremy's sperm count, expensively and plushily as it was annotated, horrified him. What he remembered of his education, under the aegis of Marion's father, was that masturbation was something only rotters did. He was shown into a room where soft music played and there were magazines which were certainly not *Country Life* or *Hare and Hound*. In one there was a picture of a long-legged girl, sweet, young and lolling. A man's hand was lying on her thigh, just temptingly approaching the pretty bit. Suddenly, he did what he had been told, by the slender nurse in a very clean uniform, to do. The plastic cup was full.

'Low sperm. Very low. Of course, it may not always have been so, but we shall never know now. But, if your wife's gynaecologist found nothing amiss with her, it may well have been the case,' said the doctor briskly. 'Don't worry about it. A lot of chaps equate their infertility with impotence. It's not so, at all. I spend half my time trying to get that fact across to chaps like you. Love your wife, do you?'

'Yes,' said Jeremy, sadly.

'There you are, then. Enjoy your love-life. Anyway, she needn't know about this, she must be near the menopause anyway.'

'She's only thirty-nine.'

'Oh. Well. Never mind.' The meeting had come to an end. The doctor straightened his impeccable cuffs, shook hands with Jeremy and pressed the button for the next privately insured patient.

On Christmas Day, Laura stuffed a monster turkey at both ends. With Ann and Len seeing to everything else, she was able to give the job her whole attention, even enjoying doing it. With chestnuts, bacon, sausagemeat, parsley-bread and chopped liver inside it, the thing finally weighed about thirty-two pounds. But at last John was carving and, though her back ached, she hadn't actually slipped a disc. Her mother, who had made an hour-long performance out of peeling the potatoes, had said, 'Well, at least I'm glad to see we're having it in the dining room.'

'Of course we are. We always do at Christmas, you know that,' said Laura, going over the potatoes again. They were full of eyes and bits of unseen skin and cut into a mixture of marbles and tennis balls.

Today, the Fenbys were just family. Laura had invited Jeremy and Marion, but Marion had been evasive. 'I think not, thanks so much, Laura. Jeremy's very tired, he seems to want to spend the day at home.' Jeremy would have been surprised to hear this.

'Well, then, come to lunch on Boxing Day. You needn't say yes or no now, it'll be cold, so no trouble either way.'

Now, John was at the head of the table, Laura at the foot. Between them were ranged Veronica, Ann and Len, Peter and Deirdre, and Judy and Luke. Laura could have wished that Judy had brought what she euphemistically described to herself as 'a friend'. That Luke came alone didn't worry her in the least. Luke was all right, and kept whatever wicked carryings-on he indulged in, in their place.

Having for her own reasons, arranged that Christmas Day should be spent alone with Jeremy, Marion prepared for it.

There was nowhere open, to go out to lunch: everywhere was closed on Christmas Day. Jeremy gave Marion a small but perfect gold chain, with a small but perfect diamond pendant. He was never mean, but this was lavish indeed. Marion gave Jeremy a book on the history of village cricket, which she had taken some trouble to obtain. She roasted a pheasant and made bread sauce. It had seemed hardly worth while to make a Christmas pudding for two, so she made, instead, brown-bread ice-cream. It was only a moderate success. By the same token, the quarter-pound slice of Stilton she had bought lacked the merriment of a whole, spooned and ported cheese. They watched the Queen's speech. 'She's terrific, isn't she?' said Jeremy.

'Yes,' said Marion, who was thinking about something else, something quite astonishing. She was pregnant. She had ignored the passing of the first month, she had been that route too many times in the past. But then, slight sickness, the swelling of the small breasts that Peter had commented upon, made her wonder. Almost to disprove such an idea, she got a kit from Boots. And the answer was yes.

Somewhere deep inside her, a little thumbnail sketch was beginning to grow. For the first time she felt, not exactly guilty about the lovely times she had been having with Peter, but aware of a consequence she had never contemplated. So long convinced that never would she have a baby, the early symptoms of her pregnancy had gone, by her, unnoticed, but now were undeniable.

As the television rumbled on through Brucey and Cilla, Marion curled up on the sofa and hugged her secret stomach. She knew what she was about to do, since the very day she had first made love with Peter, Jeremy had demanded that she make love with him. The child could be his, she lied to herself. She felt no disloyalty to Peter, nor any sense of depriving him: the greatest part of his pleasure had been in having her to himself, with no child to complicate the affair. Leaving Jeremy to nod on the sofa, she went out into her garden.

'I want this baby. I want it so much that I would lie for it, steal for it, if necessary.' For letting Jeremy believe the child was his would be stealing. The only money she had ever possessed, a small legacy from her mother, had long been spent. She had no money of her own, and no means of earning any. Jeremy had supported her in more than comfort all these years, and had been kind about her inability to give him the son he wanted. Well, after a while he had simply said no more about it, which she, knowing him, had accepted as his way of being kind.

It would be a summer baby. Marion leaned against the bare-boughed cherry tree. The big guest-room with its own bathroom would make a perfect nursery. She would get the grandest cradle Peter Jones could provide, with broderie anglaise draperies. Washable, of course, no speck of dust must come near. She didn't mind if the little creature was girl or boy, but maybe it would be better, considering the role she planned for Jeremy, if it should be a boy.

Then she whispered to the person inside her, 'But you are mine.' She knew she would readily forgo the adoration of Peter for the sake of this child. 'You are going to have a rich daddy; look at this gold chain and this diamond. You will have a nursery better than royal children have. And you'll be put down for Eton. Well, you will if you're a boy. Benenden, if you're a girl. The Princess Royal went there. But I will bring you down here, into my garden, to feed you. By the time you are born, the grass will be high, I will show you how to sniff the scent of wild rugosa while you suck.'

Somehow, perhaps because Jeremy drank a great deal of brandy, the remains of Christmas Day slipped by with Marion's secret still concealed.

Early on Boxing Day, Laura rang Marion. 'I'm sorry, so sorry,' she said, 'but I've got to cancel today. My mother's not well. I've got her in bed, and I'm trying to get hold of a doctor. But you know what it's like, over Christmas. I'm just waiting, in hope.'

Marion, who had intended to duck out of going to the Fenbys', now found herself with no alternative but to come to the rescue. 'Oh Laura, you poor thing. You must come to us.' It was simply not possible to let Laura down.

'I won't be able to. But I'd love to send the family over, if you're sure you don't mind.'

'I've got loads of stuff in the freezer, don't worry about it. I hope your mother soon feels better. Give her my love.'

'You're an angel, that's what you are. And I will. May I send over the remains of the turkey as well? I never want to see it again in this world.'

Ann and Len carved, in Marion's kitchen, the remains of the turkey. For the first time in her life, Marion served a casual meal.

'It's a nightmare, with Granny,' said Judy, chewing a bone. 'If she asks me one more time why I'm not married yet, I may kill her.'

'Don't bother,' said Luke; 'just tell her to shut up. That's what I do. *Have* you got a bloke, Jude?'

'Mind your own business.'

'All right. I say, Marion, I'm still hungry. Got any more to eat?' Suddenly, the brown bread ice-cream which had been so unfestive the day before was, in Luke's opinion, 'the best thing since sliced bread. I like the bits in it. It's like a sweet steak and kidney pie.'

'Those are raisins and sultanas,' said Marion.

'Perfect. I'll have to send my bird down to you for cooking lessons.'

Peter, with Deirdre accompanying him, was, this day, just the son of her friend Laura. This young woman is Peter's wife, my friend's daughter-in-law thought Marion. It was as though he and she had not spent time acquainting themselves with every inch, outside and in, of each other's bodies. Deirdre ate salad and said to Marion, 'I do so admire your home. These curtains are just what I would like to have. And we've not found anywhere in Bromley anything like as nice as this house.'

'I'm glad you like it,' said Marion. As she had moved into her indoors persona, she could look Deirdre politely in the face and forget, for the moment, the baby she had spoken to in the garden where it had been conceived. 'Would you like some ice-cream?'

'No, thank you. But I'm sure Peter would. He has a sweet tooth.'

Jeremy, one of those fortunate men whose hangovers are easily shaken off, was a genial host. Being at heart a cheerful fellow, he forgot his troubles for the moment and enjoyed the company. So much so that, after the guests had departed, he said to Marion, 'They're a nice lot, aren't they? And they adore you. If you ask me, Peter fancies you.'

'Oh, Jeremy, really! Don't be silly. He's a mere boy.'

'Mere boy nothing. He's a married man. Mind you, being married to Deirdre can't be much fun. I wouldn't blame him if he did look elsewhere.' Having done his own share of looking elsewhere, he changed the subject. 'I won't be going to the office this week,' he said. 'Nothing happens between now and New Year's Day. In any case, they can get me here if they want me. Is that all right with you?'

'But of course. I'm just surprised. You usually can't wait to get back to work.'

'I thought it would be nice to spend some time together.'

'Lovely, darling,' she said, and meant it. Fate seemed to be playing into her devious hands. The dishwasher was rumbling obediently in her impeccable kitchen as Marion got out a coffee cake for tea.

After tea, there was a long silence until, quite suddenly, Jeremy asked 'Have you been happy?'

The unexpected question took Marion off guard. 'You mean, lately?' she asked cautiously.

'No. I mean all along.'

'Well, of course I have. You've given me everything.'

'Except a child.'

This was a facer. 'But Jeremy, it was I who didn't give you

a child.' She was about to add, 'so far . . .' but Jeremy spoke again.

'No. You were such a little thing, delicate, I thought. I'm a stupid man. Men are, I suppose. I never, ever, thought it could be me. Stupid pride. You were a virgin and I was the big man, teaching you how to make love.'

'And you did. You showed me everything I'd been longing for.'

Jeremy did permit himself a nostalgic chuckle. 'You took to it like a duck to water, I must say.'

'So, what is all this about?' asked Marion, thinking *my child, my child.*

'Oh, I went for a check-up.'

'How come? You're not ill?'

'No. The firm likes us to be checked every year.' He could not tell her of Janet's revelation and its humiliating outcome. He had punished himself and now he fixed in his head the notion that he must not let faithful Marion suffer from the news of his extra-marital lust for a woman who wasn't, in the end, worth the tip of his wife's finger. He economised with the truth. 'They do everything, even the old willy. It seems I was unlikely ever to have fathered a child.'

Having made what he still couldn't think of as anything other than a confession, Jeremy suffered from Marion's silence. He simply did not know whether it came from anger, contempt or pity. And he certainly did not know that what Marion was saying to herself, and to the child in her body, was *I'll have to work something out.*

14

Peter had not expected to see Marion over the Christmas holiday. By nature uncommunicative, he found it easy and natural to keep his thoughts to himself, thoughts entirely of Marion. Marion, Marion, Marion. No passage of time, no past or future, just making love to Marion, with body and soul.

Deirdre didn't notice anything unusual. She was always willing, as a wife, to accept sexual intercourse, but if it did not take place she felt no great loss. A session with hairdresser or dress shop was equally satisfying, and house-hunting was all-absorbing.

Peter actually enjoyed Christmas Day. Deirdre continued to get on well with Veronica. Veronica, receiving the admiration she thrived upon, was at her best. And Veronica's best let loose the charm she was perfectly capable of when she wished. Between this and the help of her children, Laura was more relaxed than she had been for months.

Ann, Len and Luke became rowdy and giggly as they pulled the very expensive crackers brought by Judy. On this occasion, Veronica didn't even notice that Ann and Len disappeared to a bedroom for a satisfying cuddle between port and teatime. Such afternoon exercises were not in Deirdre's scheme of things, so Peter spent that hour going for a walk, wandering round the garden and dreaming of another garden, not a mile away.

The arrangements for Boxing Day were so hastily made that Peter found himself suddenly and unexpectedly obliged to kiss Marion. Everyone kissed everyone; Luke insisted on Marion's giving him a big smack under the mistletoe. 'There isn't any mistletoe,' said Marion. 'I didn't put any up.' Luke twiddled his fingers over her head so vividly that mistletoe seemed to appear.

While everyone was laughing, Peter managed to walk away and calm himself. Marion had only brushed his cheek with her lips, she hadn't even let their bodies touch. But the turmoil her nearness induced had as violent an effect on Peter as if he were once again beside her in one of their secret motel room beds.

'Are you all right, Peter?' asked Judy.

'Yes. Why?'

'You've gone white. I hope you haven't got flu or something.'

'How is Veronica?' asked Marion.

Veronica was briefly discussed, everyone agreed that this was the time of year when flu might be about, the subject was dropped and lunch was continued. Peter got through the rest of the day.

With Christmas and New Year now over, Peter longed for Marion. The first time she said she couldn't come to him didn't worry him. Even the second time, he managed to tell himself that all was well, and she would come to him soon. But as time went by, although Marion never said in so many words that she wasn't going to see him again, he could not fail to realise that such was the case. He had never felt so desolate.

And now, at last, guilt came into it. And he knew that the guilt he felt was not about being in love with Marion. It was about not being able to be in love with Deirdre. At times, he was hard pressed not to hate her. He became more and more polite. Although Deirdre would have been horrified if she had known the thoughts that Peter's manners were concealing, she was fortunately too involved in her own plans to be in the slightest bit aware of them.

Actually, Deirdre's house-hunting was a mercy, for she could talk of nothing else. All Peter had to do was to seem to listen to her. 'I've decided against Bromley. I thought Chislehurst might be worth looking into. I've got a house to see there and I'll take a look round the neighbourhood while I'm at it. And then of course, we could consider getting something old, further out, and doing it up. Marion Clark has done wonders with her house.' Deirdre greatly admired what she called Marion's life-style. She stockpiled clichés as confidently as she filled her cupboards with advertised polishes, spot-removers, carpet shampoos and washing-up liquids that made crystal dance for joy.

With a second whisky in his hand, Deirdre's voice flowed over him like the tide coming in over shingle. He thought all the time of Marion, above all of her enchanting gift for making him feel so proud of himself. It had been a particular joy to see her becoming prettier with every meeting, even a little plumper. He had read somewhere that when a woman is having a happy love affair, her breasts get bigger. And Marion's had. The real reason for this had not occurred to him.

Although love-making was not all that important to her, Deirdre prided herself on knowing her wifely duty, and offered herself up at least once a week. On these occasions, Peter forbade himself to think of Marion. Fortunately, even in his misery, nature had its way and Deirdre was content with his efforts.

Laura was out shopping in Swanmere when she saw Marion, apparently in a dream. What Marion was doing was, for the first time in her life, looking at babies in prams. Nice enough little things, but nothing like as precious as what was inside her. She was imbued with the primeval protectiveness of motherhood: her and her child versus all the rest. In the past, she had been irritated by young mothers who importantly parked their prams across shop doorways so that no one could get past. Now, she realised that precious babies must not be left out of sight for a single second.

'Hallo, Marion. You look as if you're trying to remember what you came out for.'

'Hallo, Laura.' That the baby inside her was almost certainly her best friend's grandchild drifted through her mind. But pregnancy had rendered her so dreamy that the thought just muddled itself aside.

Laura continued, 'Not that I can talk. I think *my* brain's completely gone.' At last leaving her own reveries alone, Marion realised that Laura looked completely exhausted. There were pinch-lines encroaching on her pretty mouth, and her eyes had suddenly aged.

'Are you all right, Laura? I know it's horrid to be told one doesn't look well, but you don't. You look as though you've got flu. You ought to go to bed for a couple of days.'

'Bed!' snapped Laura. 'You must be joking. You don't seriously think I could go to bed for half a day, never mind two, do you?'

'Is Veronica not better? I know she wasn't well at Christmas, but I thought she was over it.'

'There wasn't a damn thing wrong with her. Oh, I'm sorry, Marion, I shouldn't say that about my own mother but I honestly don't know how I can take any more of it.' She was very near to bitter tears.

'Look, I was just on my way home. I'm tired and I'm longing to sit down. Why don't you come with me and I'll make us a sandwich. And a glass of wine wouldn't do you any harm.' Marion suppressed the wave of nausea that the very word wine provoked, and resolutely took her friend's arm.

'I can't. Mummy will wonder where I am.'

'Let her.' With new-found feeling, Marion added, 'It's time you learned to be a bit selfish. If you go on like this you'll collapse and then you won't be any use to anyone.'

Suddenly Laura gave in and allowed herself to be led home

by Marion. Bustled into Marion's clean, warm house, she found herself seated at the kitchen table, while Marion rummaged in the refrigerator, and fetched a bottle of wine and two glasses, which she filled. Not noticing that her own glass had been refilled before Marion had taken more than a sip, Laura said gratefully, 'You really are a kind friend. You are positively mothering me.'

'And it's about time someone did,' said Marion gruffly.

Laura drained her unaccustomed midday glass. 'I feel so guilty, Marion. About Mummy, I mean. I must be unnatural but the awful truth is that it's driving me mad, having her in the house. It's my fault. I ought to be more patient, she can't help being old,' and tears began to pour down her cheeks.

'Don't cry. On the other hand, do, if you want to.'

Laura burst out laughing. 'You clever thing. I never thought of drying a person's tears by telling them to pour out more of them. Oh, Marion, what am I going to do? This could go on for years. And,' she added, looking slightly embarrassed, 'you may think it's silly, when I'm so old and John is older, but we do still like to make love. Or rather, we did. But every time John starts, she gets out of bed. The other night, she came straight into our bedroom. Said she wanted to know what time it was.' The tight lines round Laura's mouth at last relaxed into tear-dampened mirth. 'It seems only the other day some baby used to rattle on the door-handle and "wanna drinka water" and now it's Mummy. By the time this is over, my parts will have dried up like a Cape gooseberry and John's will have gone prostate from neglect. You haven't drunk your wine.'

'I'm dieting.'

'You? Dieting? You weigh seven stone on a fat day.'

'I have put on a bit of weight.'

Laura now looked as closely at Marion as Marion had, a couple of hours earlier, looked at her. 'So you have. But it suits you. Now I come to notice it, you are looking very pretty.'

Marion made up her mind. She would have to start somewhere; her condition couldn't be concealed for ever. And who better than Laura to be told? 'Actually, Laura,' she said, 'I'm not dieting. I'm pregnant.'

'Oh, Marion, how wonderful! Wait till I tell the children. Ann and Len are beginning to talk about having a baby. I'm thankful to say they intend to get married, first. I don't know about Judy. She may, she may not. But Luke will be thrilled about it. This is wonderful. You've been so good to my children. They'll all want to be godparents. Specially Peter. He adores you. Is Jeremy thrilled?'

'I haven't told him yet. I wanted to be quite sure it wasn't a mistake.' Marion had opened the first move in what was to be her campaign of deception.

For now, she wanted to be alone again, with her baby. But first she escorted Laura home to the Grange. Veronica was hovering in the hall, very cross. 'Hallo, Veronica,' said Marion. 'How are you?'

'Not well at all. And I've been alone all day.'

'Hardly all day. It's only half-past two.'

'I've had nothing to eat.'

'You know where the refrigerator is,' said Marion brutally. 'If you are going to live in someone else's house, and you are lucky enough to be free to help yourself, you should do so.'

Veronica drew herself up to her full height. 'Someone *else's* house? This is my daughter's house.'

Marion would have liked to point out that it was also John's house. But the stricken, almost frightened look on Laura's face stopped her. To her own annoyance she fell into the trap that Veronica so skilfully set for everyone, lost her nerve and burbled placatingly, 'I'm so sorry I kept Laura so long, it was all my fault, I kept her talking. So don't be cross with her.'

'Cross with her? What do you mean? I am not, and I never have been, one of those mothers who interferes in her daughter's life. Laura does exactly as she pleases.'

Before she should further abase herself by telling Veronica how marvellous she was, Marion went home.

'Your friend has put on weight,' said Veronica nastily.

'Yes. She has. She is expecting a baby.'

'Good heavens.' Veronica had not got over the rudeness just now of the woman who occupied, in her scheme of things, the position of useful admirer. 'Are you sure? She is well over forty.'

'No. She's scarcely thirty-nine.'

'Oh. Well, the child will be an idiot, of course. They always are in these circumstances.'

'Not necessarily. In any case, they have tests these days.'

'I know all about that. The papers are full of it, nothing's sacred. If there's the slightest thing wrong with the poor child, you just have an abortion. It's disgusting, if you ask me.'

Laura went to her room and tried to read a book.

It was not yet dark, although the sun, in that deceptive winter redness that it uses to keep itself warm rather than to warm the cold countryside it turns away from as fast as it can, was already setting. Marion went down into her wild garden.

By the time Jeremy came home, she was prepared. When at last he had managed to take in what Marion was telling him, he was, in his own words, knocked sideways. In short he was overcome by sheer elation. 'Bloody doctors, what a bunch of idiots. Low sperm count, indeed. Well, I may have a low sperm count, but what's the point of a million of them when it only takes one good one to do it?' He burst out laughing and looked down at his own nether regions. 'You took your time, spermo, old boy. But you got there in the end.'

Marion put her arms round him. 'I'm glad you're pleased.' ·

'Pleased? I've never been so happy in all my life.'

The next day, he came home carrying a large teddy bear.

15

At last the days began to lengthen. Veronica Chadwick, digging her fork into a salmon mousse at Marion Clark's house said contentedly, 'I've always enjoyed the coming of spring time. So promising.' She had decided to be nice to Marion, and to overlook her folly in having a baby at her time of life. 'Particularly for you,' she said, 'with the baby to look forward to.'

Having said that, and having devoured the mousse and the profiteroles that followed it, she settled down to look at the magazines, always new ones, on the table that Marion placed so conveniently within her reach, while Marion went out to make the coffee. *Vogue*. Not much use to Marion, in her condition. Veronica flipped through the fashions, and congratulated herself that she could still get into anything they showed, and her neck, she believed, was not crêpey. She did, although she would never admit to such a thing, briefly drop off. Fortunately, Marion woke her up just before the long-gone gardener rolled her over in the long-gone bedroom in which her unfortunate husband had not been welcome.

As Christmas Day drew to its close, Veronica really had felt rather unwell. Hardly surprising, taking her greed for sweet things into account. Deirdre came dangerously near to putting her foot in it, by commenting on how marvellous it was that Veronica could eat so much and never put on weight. Veronica almost, but not quite, left the rest of her trifle uneaten.

The bout of indigestion she later suffered was easily diagnosed, by Veronica herself, as a heart attack.

Dr Hallows made reassuring noises, but then that was his way. Laura had been really frightened, and was easily persuaded that what she must do was to move out of the bed she and John had so happily shared for years, and into the little nursery next to Veronica's bedroom. She was still sleeping there, even as spring drew on. She and John had not made love in all that time.

By now, Laura had got into the habit of enduring, almost without listening to them, her mother's opinions on the government, feminism, the shocking state of affairs since hanging went out, the mannerlessness of all children (including her own), foreign (black) doctors, and the scrounging habits of unmarried mothers and drug addicts.

Having negated her own existence, her one great and warm-hearted interest was in the progress of Marion's baby. Swanmere was lucky to have a doctor who was good with old people. This was because he was, himself, of an age to have been to youthful parties with most of the village's ancient survivors. Now Laura had no wish to alarm Marion, but she could not help but say delicately, 'I know we all love dear old Dr Hallows, goodness knows he's marvellous with my mother. But don't you think you ought to go to someone a little more up to date?'

'Jeremy wants me to stay with Dr Hallows, so I will.'

What Jeremy, chortling with pleasure as he stroked his wife's minuscule bump, had said was, 'You can keep these modern doctors. They don't know anything. We've proved that.'

Marion continued, 'It's what Jeremy wants for me, so it's what I want to do. And Dr Hallows is good friends with the Matron at the nursing home. He's made sure I'll have a private room and I want to go there. It's so nearby.'

Laura forbore to mention that she had given birth to Peter, her own first child, in that nursing home in luxurious agony. After that she had opted for a good National Health hospital and a ward full of other women whose stitches and sore nipples were dealt with by nurses who demonstrated their sympathy with efficiency, not words. 'Well,' she said lamely, 'I had Peter there.'

'Did you?' Marion spoke as though she could hardly remember which one of Laura's children Peter was. 'Good. That's nice. In any case, I could hardly go to any other doctor now. It would offend Dr Hallows.'

'Well, really,' said Veronica on a day early in March when Laura told her that Ann and Len had got married. 'I never heard of such a thing. Fancy getting married in Lent.'

'I don't think,' said Laura, 'that anyone takes too much notice of Lent these days.'

Veronica drew breath, just as though she had always spent Lent on her knees rather than on the knees of the gardener or the passing salesmen. 'What a hole-in-the-corner business. It should have been after Easter, and here. I should think Theodor Carew will be very disappointed. A marriage in this family should have taken place in his church. But then, on the other hand, I suppose poor Ann could scarcely produce Len (such a name) here. He wouldn't know what to wear.'

'They are very happy together,' said Laura, at last with some firmness.

'I suppose it was a shotgun wedding.' Veronica was complacently unaware of her own profound vulgarity.

Laura was engaged in making her mother a little lunch. The patience she cultivated so assiduously was not up to this unfair attack on her child. 'No. It was not. Yes, they do want children. And they want to give them a proper background.'

'You are saying I didn't?' said Veronica, spoiling for a fight.

'I am not saying anything, except that your lunch is on the table.'

Momentarily overawed, Veronica ate her lunch in silence.

Having prepared herself for at least some adverse comment on the state of the fish, Laura also remained silent.

Now that March had come in like a lamb, Marion spent a lot of time showing her as yet unborn baby her garden. Having eschewed modern medical facilities, she had no idea whether this little object was a boy or a girl, so she addressed it as 'You'. She did not consider 'You' able, yet, to understand that it had been conceived in the garden in which it would, one day, swing and play. Anyway, 'You' was now so much more real than anything else in her life that its begetting was lost in the mists of last autumn.

After a visit to the garden, she would show 'You' the nursery, which was coming on apace.

Jeremy watched the prettiness of Marion as her belly swelled. All the desire he had once felt for Janet completely faded away. He looked at Marion with affection and prided himself on having gone through that humiliating and expensive experience at the clinic. It had been on his insurance, paid for by his firm, but even so, it had been his punishment to himself. And now his reward was that the experts had been all wrong, for he had begotten a child. Having always been a man who preferred the enjoyable parts of his women, he had wisely avoided ruining pleasure with gynaecological knowledge. With his usual good fortune, his eye lit on an article in the *Daily Mail* about a couple who had been childless for the twenty years of their marriage and then, all of a sudden, lo and behold, a lovely baby arrived – 'our little miracle' – and then another one the next year.

Dr Hallows, who never made night calls these days – his patients knew better than to have their heart attacks after dark – dumped his bag at home one Friday and went down to the Beaters' Arms for a pint. He was not surprised to see Jeremy. 'Well, my boy, how's the little mother?'

'Absolutely fine. I tell her she's fat as a pig, but she isn't of course. She's looking lovely.'

'I expect you are hoping for a boy?'

'A boy would be nice, but I don't care, as long as it arrives in one piece. Just seeing Marion so happy is wonderful, and I can love a little girl just as much.'

'Good thinking. I'm dead against all this finding out the sex of the baby before it's born. I'll tell you a story. I heard of a chap who had a wife and a mistress. The wife had had a couple of daughters. And then his mistress got pregnant. Had all the tests and told him it was a boy. He'd always longed for a son, so he asked his wife for a divorce and was all set to marry the mistress and give the boy his name.' Pausing only to allow Jeremy to refill his glass, Dr Hallows continued, laughing his head off. 'Well. The little bugger must have been lying the wrong way round when they took the picture. Have you guessed? You have! It was a girl. Oh, dear dear.'

Jeremy found his plumper wife incredibly attractive. Where before she had always been on the run, tidying and cleaning, she now sometimes sat still. When he asked, humbly, if it was safe for her to be made love to, she would say 'Oh yes, that's quite all right.' He combined his passion with such gentleness that Marion found it perfectly easy to accept him. Jeremy knew her quite well enough to realise she was not getting as much as he was out of their love-making, but he simply put it down to her pregnancy. He was right, in a way. But he had no idea that she felt nothing but love for the child inside her.

Mrs Bean, who put up with that Mrs Chadwick, even when the old bat would run her finger along a just-dusted mantelpiece, solely for Mrs Fenby's sake, coiled the Hoover lead and said, 'Well, fancy!' Laura, with her mother briefly out of the way, put two mugs of coffee on the kitchen table. Mrs Bean liked hers strong, not too much milk, with two lumps of sugar. Laura, whose days were a struggle to find energy, and admiring Mrs Bean's endless bustling vigour, now put two lumps in her own mug. Mrs Bean's openings were always either 'Well, fancy!' or 'Have you heard?' 'Have you heard?' now followed.

'Heard what? Tell me, Mrs Bean,' said Laura.

'Is it true? Mrs Clark's expecting?' The questions being rhetorical, Laura was able to lean forward in silence and not spoil the story by interjecting her own pre-knowledge. 'I don't go to the Beaters' Arms, not unless it's an occasion, like it was, your lovely party. But last week, Tuesday; no, it was the Wednesday, my Reg said, all of a sudden, come and have a drink at the Beaters', he said. Well, do you know, it was my birthday and I'd forgotten every word about it. He'd got champagne on ice, think of that. It was nice; I could take to champagne. Anyway,' Mrs Bean sipped her coffee and went on, 'Ed Bagshot was there. Calls himself *Mister* Bagshot these days.'

'He does a lot of work at the Clarks' house, doesn't he?' said Laura.

'Work!' sniffed Mrs Bean. 'I wouldn't let him put a new washer on my kitchen tap, but there you are. Anyway, he's dipping into the champagne my Reg had bought for me, and he tells the assembled company he's doing a fancy nursery for the Clarks. Calls them Jeremy and Marion. Oh yes, he says, old Jeremy's brought it off at last. Never thought he could, the townie, he said. I could have hit him. Takes their money and insults them.'

'Well, it's lovely, isn't it?' said Laura.

Mrs Bean was in her stride. Now that pregnancy was on the agenda, Ed Bagshot could be forgotten. 'I hope it will be all right. I mean, at her age.'

'I think it will be all right,' said Laura.

'You knew, then? Well,' said Mrs Bean, generously, 'you would. You've been a good friend to Mrs Clark, all along.'

'I've become fond of her. And she's been a very good friend to my children.'

'She lost her own mother, didn't she? When she was only little. Sad, that. Is her father still alive?'

'I'm not sure.' Veronica now appeared in the kitchen, looking pointedly at Mrs Bean, the pointedness directed at Laura.

Mrs Bean got to her feet. 'Good morning, Mrs Chadwick,' she said. She was well aware that Mrs Chadwick would have preferred to be addressed as Madam. She could almost (but not quite) feel sorry for this tiresome old woman who was still, no doubt, irritated with her late husband for not having been knighted, in order to make her a lady. 'I'll give your bedroom a nice turn-out,' she said.

Veronica sniffed. 'Well, be careful. What little is left of my treasures, my Meissen and my precious glass. The shelf is narrow.' She looked at Mrs Bean's hands, which reddened and swelled under her cold eye. 'Please try not to break them.'

Just as Laura was wondering how she could get through the afternoon, the telephone rang. 'Mrs Fenby?'

'Yes. Speaking.'

'It's Len.'

'Oh, Len. Is everything all right?'

'I was wondering if me and Ann could come down and see you.'

'Of course. When would you like to come?' Laura bit back exhaustion.

'Tomorrow? See, the restaurant's fully booked for the weekend. But we've just got the day off tomorrow, and Ann wants to see you.'

'Do you? Want to see me, I mean?'

'Ann does. So I go along with that.'

Laura detected a note of anxiety in Len's voice. How courageous he must have been, to telephone on Ann's behalf. 'You'll *both* be more than welcome.'

'Thanks, Mrs Fenby.'

'And, Len. I am your mother-in-law now. I hope you don't mind. But, please, you can't call me Mrs Fenby. Could you, perhaps, call me Laura?'

'I don't think so. Where I come from, that would be disrespectful. I'll think of something. Thanks for saying tomorrow is OK.'

16

Laura went to the linen cupboard and got out the best sheets to make up the guest-room bed for Ann and Len. Mrs Bean, helping her, was about to mutter that Mrs Chadwick couldn't have anything to object to now, but didn't. Free as she was to say whatever she liked to Laura, she kept her mouth shut on the subject of Mrs Chadwick. Mrs Fenby had enough to put up with, without *her* opinion making matters worse. Personally, she wished the old devil would die. Well, not actually die, wishing a person dead was wicked, but a broken hip and a final move to a nursing home wouldn't do any harm.

Ann and Len arrived while Laura was casting through her deep-freeze, looking vainly for something she hoped she had once made, to give them for lunch. Straightening her back, which always seemed to ache these days, she caught sight of her face, reflected in the kitchen window. A tight-lipped woman with what she could only describe as a cross expression looked back at her. It was the face of a woman who had lost all the pleasures of generosity. The prospect of a happy family round the table, once her greatest joy, had now become a tired sigh at the thought of preparing more food. And it was the face of a woman who was no longer made love to by her husband. John's kindly uncomplaining-ness she interpreted, looking at that unattractive face, as the departure of desire for her.

She didn't even hear the large Range Rover that pulled up outside the door at twelve o'clock. Ann and Len, tumbling out, were first greeted by Veronica, looking, as Len said to himself, as though she owned the place. She also looked, costumed in pink, like a lady of the house whose servants did everything while she prepared to receive. 'Hallo, Granny,' said Ann.

'Good afternoon, Mrs Chadwick,' said Len.

Veronica peered. 'Oh,' she said, 'Leonard, is it?'

'Len,' said Len.

Laura now appeared, looking tired and wearing her glasses. Len hugged her. Veronica was obliged to step aside as he managed to push his mother-in-law ahead of her and into her own home.

Although she hadn't the faintest idea what she was going to give them to eat, Laura couldn't help but be slightly cheered by the arrival of the young people. But as John had announced that today he would be in for lunch, since Ann and Len were coming, gloom about her non-existent menu reasserted itself. She actually felt like bursting into tears.

She realised that Len was speaking to her. 'I hope you don't mind,' he said, 'but we've got rather a lot of food with us. We didn't want to be rude, but me and Ann like showing off, so we hoped you wouldn't mind. I've made a vegetable terrine, and a watercress soup. They're in the chiller box, so they're quite safe. And there's my own salad that I grew, and a bottle of my dressing. And Ann's apple and apricot tart. And chef gave me a cold Châteaubriand.'

Laura did, now, burst into tears. Len pushed her out of sight of Veronica. 'Come on,' he said, 'you can't be that sorry your daughter's married me. I'm not that bad.'

'Oh Len! And you and Ann did more than half the Christmas cooking.'

'We like doing it,' said Len.

Lunch went on for a very long time. John, whose toleration of his mother-in-law survived by the simple method of his keeping out of the way for most of the day, now celebrated this happy occasion by bringing out good wines. Veronica remained upright throughout. Ann had long kicked off her shoes and was wriggling her toes against Len's ankles.

Veronica, whose feet were by now agonisingly hitting the sides of her beige court shoes (beige, not white, white was so common) hung on until Len said, 'Well, I don't know about anyone else, but me and Ann could do with a lie-down.'

Veronica tottered up to her room and lay down. Really, the way he spoke! And bed in the afternoon, what a thing! It was a very long time since Veronica's afternoon beddings had been succeeded by greed. She consoled herself by thinking how awful it was for poor Ann to have married a man of such low origins. She drifted off to sleep. But in her dreams, Veronica's body escaped and flew free, back to the world old age had deprived her of. Of course it was not of her late husband that she dreamt, but of lovers who had become aristocratic in memory. She was beautiful and smooth, she had a 22-inch waist and a lovely bosom. She did not call her bosom breasts. It had been called, by the gardener, 'smashing tits' and by the double-glazing salesman, 'big boobs'.

John, in a jolly mood, went off to a vestry meeting. Greeting Theodor Carew, he was able to broach the subject he had so far shied away from. 'You heard my wicked child went off and got married without benefit of clergy?' he said.

Theo, though not lucky enough to have had several glasses of lunchtime wine, but a gallant Christian nevertheless, responded in equally jovial tones, 'They will do it. Pity, I love weddings. But still, let us be thankful they have at least got married. I've almost come to believe that any form of marriage is better than none. God bless them.'

That out of the way, John sat through the agenda of falling Sunday School numbers and rising damp, with an expression of deep concentration on his face. It was genuine; he was concentrating on not falling asleep.

Veronica, her dream-lovers fled away, awoke in a bad mood. She lay in her bed, telling herself that of course Laura would forget to bring her tea, with Ann and Len in the house.

Now, cross with unhappiness, she said to herself, 'Goodness, how she has let herself go. At her age I was still a pretty woman, not old and drawn like she is. It's not as though she had a hard life, specially now the children are grown up and with me here to help.'

Veronica had never seen her inability to love as a disadvantage, largely because she was entirely unaware of any such lack in herself. She could not see that Laura was still in love with John, and he with her, nor that Ann and Len were bonded by love for each other. Nor could she see that Laura's abiding love for her children was a mother-love she had, herself, never received. Veronica had known nothing of the sweet exchanges made, in bed, between true lovers. She had considered herself generous to have allowed her husband into her bed. She had dressed her daughter charmingly and herself elegantly when attending school functions, at which she expected to be told that Laura was a pretty child but would never be a beauty like herself. Laura had never been lifted on to her mother's lap.

Veronica's middle-aged escapades would have been describable, in a vernacular outside of her vocabulary, as 'having sex'. Love was what she had never made.

Laura, born with a loving heart, merely felt guilty and confused by her inability to make Veronica happy. She was aware that her mother despised her, and blamed herself, always feeling in the wrong. She was unable to see that her mother was a bully and, like all bullies, despised her victims.

Everyone re-gathered in the evening. John had eschewed sleep, and gone for a long walk after the vestry meeting. Laura had at least managed to have a sneaky read. Ann and Len tumbled downstairs, floppy with love-making.

'I'm hungry,' said Len. 'And I bet you are, too, Mrs Chadwick.'

'I had no tea, certainly,' said Veronica.

'Oh, Mummy, I'm sorry. I forgot,' said Laura.

'Never mind.'

'May I make omelettes, Mum?' said Len. 'Sorry, perhaps you don't like being called Mum.'

'I like it very much.'

'We went to see Peter and Deirdre,' said Ann.

'Good, I'm glad,' said John. 'They haven't been down for a while. How are they?'

'All right. Peter was a bit quiet.' She forbore to add that her brother had looked thoroughly miserable. 'They still haven't been able to find a house they like. Peter doesn't seem to know what he wants, and Deirdre wants what they can't afford. Poor Peter.'

'What do you mean, "Poor Peter"? Why shouldn't Deirdre want a nice house? She's a very good wife. You young women, these days, with your own careers. Deirdre says that her career is looking after her husband. And quite right, too. The world would be a better place if more girls were like her.' Veronica was as near being fond of Deirdre as her cold heart allowed. They were sisters under the skin, and Deirdre had been quick to recognise an ally.

'Darling, you know Marion and Jeremy are expecting a baby, don't you?' said Laura to Ann. 'Isn't it lovely?'

Ann, who was glad to get away from the subject of Deirdre (she and Luke had compared caustic notes) said, 'Lovely.'

'I hope it will be all right,' said Laura. 'At her age, I mean.'

'Of course it will. Everyone has babies in their thirties, even their forties, these days. Look at Patricia Hodge.'

'You're not waiting that long, my friend, if I've got anything to do with it,' said Len. 'Think of your mum. You'd like to be a granny, wouldn't you, Mum?' Unkindly, he added, 'You'd like to be a great-grandmother, wouldn't you, Mrs Chadwick?'

Veronica went to bed. The long-ago lovers she had dreamt of earlier did not come back.

17

In Marion's garden, the snowdrops came and went. Because of its strange, wild nature things bloomed out of season, wrapped in the warmth of the weeds that didn't know they were weeds. A rose that had never felt the touch of a pruning knife would suddenly dangle a small bud just as the aconites were opening.

Her baby was very good. It would give a gentle little wriggle, just to show it was there, and then settle down, as though it already had its thumb in its mouth. It was not a heavy baby; it curled up neatly within its mother's small frame.

Jeremy no longer saw Janet. He had dropped her as ruthlessly as Marion had dropped Peter. Being out of Jeremy's picture was hard on Janet, but not half as hard as being out of Marion's was on Peter.

As the year wore on through its first quarter and Marion evaded him, the dream in which he had lived was routed by painful reality. What kind of a fool had he been, to think he could live a double life? All the confidence he had gained, during the months of happiness which Marion had given him, was gone. The sense of humour she had uncovered in him now went back into its shell. Privately he mocked himself, which was the only way in which he could bear his misery. He remembered how Mrs Bean, when dismissing people she considered to be above themselves, would say, hands round her coffee mug and head nodding, 'Who do they think they are?'

Who indeed, Peter asked himself, did he think he was? A

seducer? Seducers did not fall in love. Jeremy Clark was a seducer. Physical unfaithfulness meant nothing to him for the simple reason that he loved, and would never wish to lose, his own wife. Jeremy had had the good fortune to marry the right woman whereas he, Peter, had not.

'We really must find a house soon,' said Deirdre. 'I mean, how can I entertain for you here, in this poky little flat? I know a house in town is out of the question, and Chislehurst was no good in the end.' Deirdre's ambitions were growing by the day, and Chislehurst had now joined Bromley as an impossible suburb. 'But we could get a really nice property in Swanmere.'

'Swanmere?' said Peter, thinking how little he could bear to live in Swanmere, now that Marion no longer wanted him. He had had to accept that fact. Even if she answered his telephone calls, she simply evaded his suggestions of a meeting.

'If it's entertaining you're thinking of, you can't expect London clients to come to Swanmere for dinner,' said Peter.

'Weekends,' said Deirdre firmly. 'House parties.' For a woman of the nineties, Deirdre, not usually fanciful but under the influence of Veronica, was oddly able to re-create a chimera of the fifties. Peter went to the refrigerator. 'What are you looking for?' asked Deirdre, who was wearing an expensive outfit, and whose hair was impeccable. Her hair-dos were always a little dated; she had no time for Fergie-messiness.

'A beer,' said Peter.

'All right, then. But don't open the champagne. They're having it here, before we go out.' Peter had forgotten that they were going out, or who they were going out with, and didn't dare to ask. 'You'd better have a shower and get changed first,' said Deirdre.

He let the shower run over his shoulders, no longer wanting the beer. The hot water flowed all over him. Once, he had showered with Marion. He emerged, with a towel wrapped around him. 'Darling,' he said, dishonest in the use of the appellation but knowing that what he wanted was relief, sheer, brute, animal mounting. 'Come and kiss me. I mean, come and make love to me.'

'I will, later,' said Deirdre, putting out nuts. 'Not now. Mind my dress.'

They dined at a restaurant that Deirdre had read about in the *Evening Standard*. The sorrel sauce was nauseating, the wine was worth three pounds a bottle and cost twenty-five. His guests were, Deirdre had assured him, useful possible clients. Clients for what? I am just, thought Peter, some sort of an insurance salesman, dressed up as a broker.

Deirdre was at her best. 'You must,' she told the balding man on her right hand, 'have the bread-and-butter pudding.' The balding man was not in the habit of being taken out to dinner in order to eat bread-pudding, but he supposed it was the in thing, so he accepted it. His wife, a decent woman, would have liked a vanilla and strawberry ice-cream, but she was striving to be smart. She settled for *crème brûlée*, which was quite nice, even though she had to put the topping aside on account of her teeth.

Deirdre Fenby was so well dressed. Low-heeled sandals. The wife went home and threw her new pair of court shoes into the cupboard. 'Peter doesn't talk much, does he?' she said to her husband. Her husband didn't reply; he was trying to brush the bread-pudding out of his teeth, which were in no better state than hers.

Peter, reflecting on the colossal bill he had just paid, did what he always did as he undressed, which was to tip the change from his trouser pocket into a bowl on the dressing table. Deirdre did what she always did, which was to wince at the clatter it made, just as Peter was working out something nice to say about her success at dinner. She was examining her upper lip in the mirror. 'I had a phone call from your mother,' she said. 'We haven't been down there for quite a while. I think she'd like us to go. Veronica likes me, you know. I hate to say this, but your mother isn't very good at handling Veronica. But I understand her.' The lip seemed to pass muster and Deirdre looked content.

'Of course,' said Peter, only too happy to oblige. He placed the blame for his unhappiness squarely where it belonged: on himself. 'Any other news?' he asked, for the sake of something to say.

'Let me think. Oh yes, the Clarks. They're expecting a baby. After all these years.' Deirdre now arranged herself in bed. Having repelled her husband's advances when she was dressed to go out and do him good, she was now ready to give him his dues. But he seemed to have gone to sleep. She glanced at an article in the *Reader's Digest* and then settled down beside him.

But, thought Peter, lying awake, there was not to be a child. Marion was my private person. I cannot bear to think of her, heavy in that way. She's so little. Those tiny breasts, those pretty arms. All that kindness. She was like a little girl, and I the man.

That her husband was not in love with her was lost on Deirdre. She thought he was. If asked, she would have used the words 'in love' in the same context as she used such phrases as 'life-style' and 'state-of-the-art'. She was fortunate in her talent for simplifying life with jargon. Peter and she were married; married people were 'in love'. And, if any proof were needed, it was there, demonstrated by the fact that he gave her presents, and was always courteous to her.

Young Mr and Mrs Fenby were to pay an Easter visit to Swanmere. Laura did her best to feel pleased. She stocked the deep-freeze and tried not to panic at the thought of three whole days of lunches, dinners and, worst of all, breakfasts. There was no hope of Ann and Len coming to the rescue. They would be run off their feet at the restaurant. Ann, who often telephoned her mother, encouraged by the warmth between her and Len, called and told her, 'You know kids,

Ma? No, not me, not yet, hang on. It's that we have to let them in, now that the pubs are doing it. So we've got to organise an Easter-egg hunt. I was going to make chocolate eggs myself but Head Chef said no. I thought he'd be pleased, but d'you know what he said? He said, and I quote, "I'm not wasting you on that riff-raff. You make a simnel cake and I'll send out for a bargain bag of *oeufs-nausées*, which they'll love."'

Laura wanted the visit to be a success. To this end, she decided to invoke Marion. But Marion let her down. This came as a surprise. As Marion's pregnancy advanced, Laura had been to see her, to ask if Veronica's visits were not getting to be too much for her, and had been told, 'Certainly not. I've never felt better in my life.' In fact, Marion's energy at this time was phenomenal. On more than one occasion, she had even taken Veronica to visit stately homes and gardens, visits from which Veronica had returned in a good mood, having bored the guides to death with tales of how she had known the places before the public was let in.

Now Laura walked over to Marion's house. Remembering how good Marion had been, that last Boxing Day, having the whole family when Veronica had had her 'turn', she had worked out a scheme whereby the Clarks would come to the Fenbys on Saturday night and, she hoped, have them all to lunch after church on Sunday. Deirdre would want to go to church. Laura tried hard not to be grudging about Deirdre, to tell herself that Deirdre's determined efforts to fit into Swanmere were her own way of showing affection for Peter.

Marion made coffee. Laura came to the point. 'Can you and Jeremy come to supper on Saturday evening? I hope you can. And there's something else. Could you give us lunch on Sunday?' Marion was on the verge of saying yes, of course, when Laura continued, 'Peter and Deirdre are coming down for the weekend.'

'Oh, Laura, no, I can't. I'm sorry. I've gone right off cooking. It's all I can do to have something for Jeremy, when he gets home. I get so tired. I am sorry.'

This was understandable. Laura cast her mind back to her own long-ago pregnancies. She remembered how tired she had got. And she had been many years younger than Marion now was. 'Of course, I understand. But you'll come to us on Saturday evening?'

'I don't think so. It's sweet of you. But I go to bed early these days.'

Laura went home, completely unable to understand what she had just heard. She had virtually been brushed off by the kind friend who had already engaged to have Veronica over in the ensuing week.

Peter and Deirdre arrived on the Saturday morning. Knowing that Peter liked the Clarks, Laura was disappointed to have to tell her son that they would not be seeing them this weekend. Peter said nothing.

Looking forward to a dull Saturday evening, the household was suddenly electrified by the arrival of Luke. He tumbled out of a racy sort of a car, driven by a leggy girl. On closer inspection, the girl, gorgeous as she was, was some three or four years older than him. 'Got any grub for us, Mum?' said Luke. 'This is Mary.'

Veronica was in her element. She had already spent the afternoon in conclave with Deirdre, of whom she approved. That Luke had looked after her, and actually given her a lot of fun while John and Laura were on holiday, was a rapidly forgotten episode, especially since he had now appeared with a woman whom she could describe as no better than she should be.

'Luke,' said Laura, overwhelmed with delight to see her youngest. 'Are you staying?'

'No way. We're booked in at the pub. I knew Pete was coming down. You've got a full house. Give us a bit of pie and then we'll be off.'

So far, Mary had not spoken. Laura was predisposed to be suspicious of her. She was so well groomed. 'There's only stew for supper,' she said, downgrading quite a decent casserole in the face of this daunting person.

'Stew?' said Mary. 'What kind of stew?'

'Mutton.'

'Not mutton? Not really mutton. Oh, the bliss!' Deirdre, outshone by the glamorous Mary, comforted herself by thinking how affected she sounded. 'May I have a big helping? I'm so hungry, you can't believe. We didn't have any lunch. Luke never eats . . .'

'Yes, I do,' said Luke, 'but lunch without wine is out of the question, and you did make me drive the last bit.'

In the end it was quite late before Luke and Mary left, by which time Deirdre was as jealous of Mary as Veronica was disapproving of her. Before leaving, Mary added to her non-Brownie points by saying to Laura, 'Please, won't you all come and have lunch with us at the pub, tomorrow? Luke and I had already decided to stay on for their Sunday lunch. I love pub roasts. And I know, if I tell them tonight, they'll fit us all in. Do say yes.'

'All of us? Are you sure?'

'Certainly. Please say you will.'

Laura, thinking how lovely it must be to earn the sort of money Mary obviously did, gratefully replied, 'Yes. And thank you very much. Don't think it's an ungracious acceptance, but I'm always delighted to eat something I haven't seen raw.'

'I don't often let rooms,' said the landlady, Betty. 'Only to people I know, specially anyone belonging to Mrs Fenby. There's three rooms up there, all got clean sheets, so you just choose what you like.' To her husband she later added, 'No problem there, there'll only be one bed to change, afterwards.'

The Beaters' Arms always did a roaring trade on Sunday lunches, and Easter Sunday was no exception. The landlady was pushed to fit five extra guests in with Luke and Mary. Quite a bit of table-juggling was necessary, but she did it. Half of Swanmere had booked, including Jeremy and Marion

Clark. Knowing how friendly the Clarks were with the Fenbys, the landlady debated for a moment putting them at the same table. But then, tact prevailing, she reminded herself that they were not Mary and Luke's guests, and so gave them a nice table for two right next to the big table.

The Fenby party were all seated when Peter, who had his back to the door, felt a tingle. He felt almost giddy; Marion's garden floated into his inner eye. Luke, opposite him and facing the door, saw Marion and Jeremy Clark come in. He also saw that Peter did not finish his smoked salmon, nor his plate of roast beef.

The landlady of the Beaters' Arms had established a tradition of getting her customers to go into the lounge for coffee. It allowed her to clear the tables without throwing the guests out, and did wonders for the brandy trade.

Laura was pleased to sit beside Marion. The very fact that Jeremy had brought her out for lunch proved that she really had not been up either to entertaining, or to coming out at night. 'Peter,' she said, 'isn't it lovely about the baby? Wouldn't it be lovely if all four of you were to be godparents?'

'What a great idea,' said Jeremy. 'With a middle-aged mum and dad, four lovely young godparents. I can't think of anything nicer.'

'I wonder,' said Luke to Mary, hours later, in her flat. They had pushed their luck, driving back to it after so bibulous a lunch.

'What do you wonder, piglet?' asked Mary.

'About that baby. I wonder if it is Jeremy's.'

'Really, don't be scandalous. If ever I saw a faithful wife, she's it.'

'You're probably right. It's just that I'm pretty certain old Pete's in love with her.'

'That doesn't necessarily mean they've been to bed together. Not everyone's as importunate as you. Not that I'm complaining.'

Luke put the matter out of his mind.

18

Although she was well on in her pregnancy, the month of April found Marion still not very big. But Jeremy pretended she was enormous, and stroked her stomach at every opportunity. 'I'll have to make you go on a diet, after all this is over. I wonder whether we've got a boy or a girl in there?'

'Dr Hallows is right, it's best not to know who it is,' said Marion evasively.

'We'll have to start thinking about names. We've got a rich choice, if the Fenby clan are all going to be godparents. I like that idea, don't you? Judy or Ann if it's a girl, Luke or Peter if it's a boy. I think Judy's a prettier name than Ann. Which do you like best, Luke or Peter?'

'I really don't know,' said Marion getting up from the sofa where Jeremy had made her sit.

'Don't run away.'

'I have to stretch my legs,' said Marion. 'I get cramp.'

Although Laura had long given away her pram, cradle and cots, she still had a store of baby clothes. Her sentimental attachment to these little garments had transcended her usual casual housewifery. They had all been laundered, pressed and folded carefully in tissue paper. She was taking them, one by one, from the chest where they were stored, when her mother appeared.

'What are you doing with those?' she enquired.

'I was thinking of Marion's baby. I remember Judy, in this smock. She could just walk. She loved it. She held up the skirt and said, "Pretty." And Peter, in these little shorts. I'm glad I saved them.'

'If you're thinking of Marion, I wouldn't bother,' said Veronica. 'You'd do better giving them to Oxfam. If you haven't seen the nursery, I have. She must have bought up the baby-linen departments of Harrods and Peter Jones put together.'

Laura remembered how Peter, when he was born, came home in a gown supplied by the nursing home. She had been too afraid, until he was really there, alive and blinking in her arms, to buy his baby clothes. And Veronica certainly hadn't been the sort of expectant grandmother who knitted shawls. 'Oh well,' she now said, folding the things back into the chest, 'maybe Mrs Bean would like them for a grandchild. Her daughter's expecting again.'

'Highly unlikely,' sniffed Veronica. 'Those sort of people wouldn't give you a thank-you for second-hand goods.'

Laura suddenly snapped. 'Don't be so nasty, Mummy.'

'Nasty? I don't know what you mean,' Veronica calmly replied. 'I simply face facts. Marion has, as I've just said, enough clothing for triplets. I wasn't being unkind. In fact, it's quite understandable. Having waited so long, she's enjoying all this part.'

Laura suppressed a sigh and gave in. Veronica, screening off her unkind reference to Mrs Bean, had won as usual. And, as usual, Laura felt awful for thinking in terms of winning and losing, with her own mother. She forced a smile and said something pleasant.

She did, for once, get some reward. A couple of days later, Mrs Bean, who was giving the landing a good doing, said, 'What do you keep in this chest, Mrs Fenby? Blankets? If it's blankets, we ought to have a go-through, in case there's moths.'

Laura opened the chest. 'Well, I never,' said Mrs Bean. 'Aren't they lovely! That little frock, all hand-smocked. They don't do them like that these days, do they?'

'I've been wondering what to do with them,' said Laura. 'I thought of Mrs Clark, but my mother tells me she's got lots. I don't suppose,' she said hesitantly, 'any of it would be any use to your Sheila?'

'She'd be thrilled. It's a little girl she's expecting. They told her on the scan, the other day. Wonderful, isn't it?' Mrs Bean was very proud of Sheila, whose second child had the same father as the first. In fact she was even married to him. She was a considerate girl, too. To please her mum, she had married Darren before the first baby, although she would have preferred to wait until after, when she could have got into a nice white wedding dress.

Pleased with this outcome, Laura had no idea that she had been on the verge of offering Marion clothes that had once been worn by her baby's father, uncle or aunts.

By now, Jeremy was getting home to Swanmere every evening. His colleagues at the office, men mostly younger than him but already fathers of teenagers, jeered sagaciously. 'You wait, my lad. Once the midnight yowling begins, you won't be so anxious to run home.' One, whose name was Terry, added, 'And watch it with this new man lark. My old lady tried it on. She would've had me up doing the two-o'clock feed. I told her my milk had dried up.' Terry chuckled appreciatively at his own witticism.

Marion now played cat and mouse with her husband. From the moment he entered the house he followed her about, wanting her to sit down, wanting to wait on her. Although unshaken in her resolute deception, his devoted attention embarrassed her. She compromised by behaving as well as she could. Jeremy found her gentle and affectionate, and blessed the baby. He knew he was far prouder of it than he would have been if it hadn't taken so long.

'You know,' he said, 'I've been thinking. After this one is born, we ought to have another. Not until you're strong enough, of course. But I mean, now that we've broken the dam, so to speak. You were an only child, and so was I. Even more to the point, it's going to be a teenager with a mum in her fifties and a dad pushing sixty. So it's only fair to give it a chum.' He had no idea that Marion was not listening to a word he was saying. He talked to her such a lot these days, he hardly watched television at all.

She took to saving up the crossword puzzle for evenings. She scarcely opened the newspaper during the day, in any case. In her precious hours alone, she spent the time stroking the piles of clothes, little sheets, cradle-muslins and washable soft toys that grew in the nursery like a hoard. After that, she would wander for hours in her garden. She had to remind herself to have lunch. Jeremy would always ask if she had eaten. She sublimated the massive lie she was living by being meticulous in this matter, and always made herself swallow at least some soup, in spite of the fact that she never felt hungry.

She now had Veronica over at least twice a week, sometimes even three times. Veronica was selfish and dishonest, and very easy to get along with. The sort of attention she needed did not require thought, only listening. Of Laura she saw less and less. She did not ask herself why. She did not ask herself why anything.

April went out sunny, and May came in rainy. But Marion didn't mind rain. Whenever she could, she went down into her garden. The rain did it nothing but good. It was wonderfully green and grateful, not rank at all. It smelt heavenly. The rich perfume of the dark red roses, the icy, almost lily-of-the-valley-like aroma of the wandering white rose drifted through the air as the sun came out.

Her baby was born where it had been conceived. Its birth was not very painful; it just slipped out, with no life in it at all. It had always been a quiet baby. It was born quietly, and never drew breath. Marion rolled over on to her side and kissed the little corpse. It was still attached to her by its umbilical cord when she was found.

It was Jeremy who found her. He had come back from his day's work and found his house empty. But he knew where his wife would be. He was right: she was in her garden.

19

Jeremy's first thought was that Marion was dead. He stood in the rain in her garden, in shock. It was only when he had managed to get down on his knees, touch her, and find that she was still breathing, that he put his hands on the baby. It was lifeless. But now he hoped that if Marion was alive, so maybe was his child. He folded them both in his arms, mother and baby, and carried them up to the house. The burden was not heavy, but he was almost in a state of collapse as he fell on to the sofa in the drawing room. He managed to reach out for the telephone that sat on the end-table.

Dr Hallows, long accustomed to the slow, stoical decline of Swanmere's elderly ladies and gentlemen, had seen nothing like this since his long ago house-surgeon days in Whitechapel. He actually snapped at Jeremy, 'You should have called an ambulance, not me.'

Jeremy snapped back, 'Call one, then.' He had been sitting for almost an hour, cradling Marion and her dead baby in his arms. Ridiculously, he whispered to her, 'I'm sorry about your lovely sofa, darling, it was as far as I could carry you.'

The pale carpet and the sofa were bloodied and ruined. Marion, quite still on his lap, looked as dead as the poor little object that was still attached to her. With his arms full of tragedy, it did not seem farcical to Jeremy to be worrying about what Marion would have to say when she saw the mess he had made of her beautiful drawing room. Only when the ambulance crew gently unlocked his hands and took their contents away did he see that the baby was a boy. It was no bigger than a glove, but very obviously a boy. Bereft of his armful, he wailed. This was his son, his dead son.

For all their haste to get Marion away, one of the men took the time to say to Jeremy, 'Don't come with us. Come to the hospital later. She'll be glad to see you then, when you've got yourself cleaned up.'

Jeremy sat on, as though he had been crippled. At last, realising that his suit, shirt and shoes were in as dreadful a state as the furniture, he stripped to the skin and went upstairs to the bathroom, leaving his clothes on the sofa. At least, he thought, I won't spoil the rest of the house.

It wasn't until the next day that Laura, coming in with Mrs Bean to do the only thing they could think of, which was to try and clear up, discovered that he had had to haul himself upstairs by the bannisters, which were covered with blood from his hands.

Dr Hallows's advice to Jeremy was to get back to work right away. 'Believe me, the hospital's doing everything for your wife. You'll be much better off at the office. Take your mind off it all.'

For the first time in his life, Jeremy felt no interest in what had always been his main concern, which was making money. There was no point in it now. But there was no room for him in his home, where Mrs Bean had taken charge and even Veronica Chadwick had turned up to move the china figurines out of the way, a task which only she, of course, understood. And walking out in Swanmere brought him looks of sympathy that he could not bear. For want of anything better to do, he dragged himself up to London and to the office.

Oddly enough, it turned out that Dr Hallows was right. It was the only area of consolation. One of the younger men patted him on the arm and said, 'Sorry about your news, Jeremy. My wife lost one. Rotten business. Don't worry about it, though. We went on and had three after that.' There was something comforting about being treated by a man still under thirty as though he and Marion still had all the time in the world.

Of all people the dreadful Terry, who considered picking up the bill to be a sign of weakness, took one look at Jeremy on the second day of his return and marched him out to have a drunken lunch, for which he paid *in toto*. His compassion knew no bounds. Having got Jeremy thoroughly sozzled, he advised him not to come back for the afternoon.

Hardly knowing what he was doing, Jeremy just walked. In the pretty garden at the foot of Villiers Street, he was importuned. 'You look lonely, dear.'

'I am,' he sighed. The importuner was a man. 'Very lonely.'

'I can help you there.'

Normally, a male prostitute would have brought out, in Jeremy, savage opprobrium and threats of calling the police. Now, he merely said, 'No, thank you. Don't let me waste your time. I'm not gay.' Gay, he thought, was the last thing he was, or ever would be. 'My wife is ill and my baby is dead.'

'Oh dear! Sorry about that.' Losing not a further moment, the young man checked his eyelashes and moved on.

With drunken rationality Jeremy decided to go to Simpson's and buy a suit to replace the one upon which Marion's blood had been spilled. After one look, he lost interest in new suits. Maybe he would buy shirts. He went out of Simpson's back door and into Jermyn Street. Jermyn Street reminded him of something.

Janet. In the midst of all his misery, Jeremy felt randy. It would serve Janet right. Janet, who had lied to him, deceived him. But Janet had been proved wrong. He *had* fathered a child, albeit a dead one. And it would be nice to knock her off, to fuck her to a standstill, and to screw her all ends upward. He strode to the door of her apartment house. Hers was Flat 5. But not any more. Flat 5 had a different name on its label.

★

When Laura rang the hospital, she knew at once that Marion was very ill. The first question was 'Are you a relation?' She lied. 'Yes, though distant. But her own mother is dead. I am *in loco parentis.*' This impressive statement seemed to suffice. She was to be allowed to visit.

In fact, by the time she reached Marion's bedside, the nursing staff seemed to regard her as Marion's mother. Heaven knows, thought Laura, I look old enough these days. Marion, quiet and pale and small, one arm strung up to a saline and glucose drip, the other attached to a blood transfusion apparatus, looked like a wax doll, pitifully neat and tidy. Laura held her hand. Marion recognised her.

The Ward Sister, who had frequently given of her time to far less likeable relatives than this decent Mrs Fenby, took Laura into a side room. 'She is recovering. I don't think she quite realises that her baby is not alive. That's not unusual. But she has a lovely husband. Well, you know that, don't you? Don't worry too much. They may manage another. He's more heartbroken than she is, at the moment. Poor man, finding her like that, out in the garden. How long she had been there, we don't know.'

Sister, who still resolutely wore a lace cap and even more resolutely refused to wear the plastic label with which she had been issued by management, a label inviting patients to address her by her Christian name, patted Laura's hand and went about her business. Laura went back into the ward and sat on beside Marion.

Marion, seeing tears gathering in Laura's eyes, reached out a hand, as best she could with all the attached paraphernalia. 'Don't cry,' she whispered.

'I'm sorry,' said Laura, wiping her eyes. 'I should be comforting you.'

'It's all right. I'm quite comfortable.'

In recognising that Jeremy was more heartbroken than Marion, the Ward Sister was right. In fact Marion's stay in the hospital, prolonged by a necessary trip to the operating theatre, became a puzzle to the staff. They were prepared for tears, but waited for them in vain.

As her physical strength improved, and she was allowed out of bed, Marion seemed able to stroll past other people's babies without a pang. She smiled when her husband visited, and sat quietly, with her hand in his. But she kept her own counsel. For only she knew that *now* her baby was safe, for ever. He would never fall and hurt himself. He would never do badly at school; no one would ever be cross with him. He would never fail to come up to the standards that Jeremy would set for 'his' son.

On the day that Marion Clark was discharged, the Ward Sister kept an eye on her. Now, if ever, the awful moment of leaving hospital without a bundle in her arms would bring her bereavement home to her.

Jeremy presented the nurses with expensive boxes of chocolates. Marion shook hands and said 'Thank you', like a polite child leaving a tea-party. 'You would have thought,' said Sister to Staff Nurse, 'that her baby didn't mean anything to her at all.'

'Maybe it didn't,' said Staff Nurse. 'You could see the husband was heartbroken, all right. But she's the fussy sort, couldn't bear her bedside table out of order, and always straightening the sheets. Perhaps she wasn't so keen. I bet her house is like a magazine.' And then, in the way of hospitals, the departing patient upon whom all care had been lavished was forgotten.

Before Marion came home, Mrs Bean, who hadn't been able to get rid of Mrs Chadwick, had decided to make use of her. 'Now,' she said, 'it's not my place to decide, but some-one's got to say the word. This carpet, this sofa, they're past praying for. If it was left to me, it would be on to the bonfire.'

'Industrial cleaners?' suggested Veronica airily, having had quite enough of all this. 'Get industrial cleaners.'

'What's industrial cleaners? I don't know what you mean,' said Mrs Bean.

Veronica didn't know what she meant, either. Moving the china ornaments was one thing, but this mess should surely be Mrs Bean's business. She left.

Laura, in agreement with Mrs Bean, settled on the bonfire. She asked Jeremy if she might do what she thought best. Jeremy said yes, of course she could.

'Pity Sheila can't help, she's such a strong girl,' said Mrs Bean, pulling up the carpet. 'But I couldn't let her, not with her baby only a month off, and we don't want another mishap. This sofa, how are we going to lift it?'

'How about Mr Bagshot?'

'Him?' Mrs Bean was truly amazed at such a suggestion.

'Well, he's earned a lot of money in this house.'

'Forget it,' said Mrs Bean, and lugged the sofa out.

The flames almost engulfed Marion's garden.

When Jeremy brought Marion home, he took her straight up to bed, so that she should not see, in her drawing room, the absence of sofa and carpet. He had gone to a lot of trouble to order identical replacements.

'These are new, aren't they?' asked Marion, vaguely, when Jeremy eventually permitted her to come downstairs.

He settled her on the sofa and knelt, his head in her lap. 'Darling, I'm so sorry.'

'What are you sorry about, Jeremy?'

'The baby. You were too ill to be told. But there was something wrong with him. It was his lungs. He would never have been able to breathe. I can never forgive myself.'

It had been a long time since Marion Clark had looked closely at her husband. She still didn't touch him, but she said, wonderingly, 'Never forgive yourself? Why?'

'The baby. You always wanted children. Well, so did I. But you're a woman, it was worse for you. And then, at last, we were having one and I was so pleased. But all I had done was to make a baby with something wrong with it, and nearly kill you, into the bargain.'

'But darling, the baby's lungs may have come from me.

146

They certainly didn't come from you.'

'How can you be so sure?'

This, thought Marion, is my husband. This is the man who taught me how to make love. This is the man who gave me my beautiful home, made a spoilt wife out of me, showed his love by letting me have everything I wanted. Now, at last, she touched him. Very gently she put her hands on his shoulders. For better, for worse, for the first time in months, she spoke the truth. 'It wasn't your baby,' she said.

20

She was deranged. There could be no other explanation of such a ridiculous statement. Jeremy's first reaction was pity. After all, who knew better than he what the poor girl had been through? Near death herself, and still attached to her dead baby. After pity, came fear. He knew it was called post-natal depression these days, but what Jeremy really feared was that his caring, capable wife had gone mad.

Faced with what he could only see as female insanity, Jeremy humbly faced the realisation that he really knew very little about women. In bed, yes, fine, that was an area he understood; an area in which he had always been confident. And as housewives, fine too, organising a daytime world of which men, the breadwinners, knew nothing. Having no idea how to cope with this disaster, he made the only suggestion he could think of, and asked, 'Would you like me to get Laura?'

'Certainly not,' said Marion. She, looking at Jeremy's fraught expression, was frightened in her turn of what she had done. She had only wanted to reassure him that the death of the baby had nothing to do with him. Now, whether she had got it wrong or not, she felt impelled to continue. 'Laura's the last person I want to see at the moment,' she said.

'Why? She's your best friend, isn't she? And you are not well.'

'I'm perfectly well.'

'Then why are you talking nonsense?'

'I'm not. I'm sorry, Jeremy. I was only trying to tell you the baby had nothing to do with you. I didn't want you to think you had passed on some defect.'

'Very well, then, if I wasn't his father, who was?' He was trying to humour her, but succeeded only in sounding impatient.

Marion's words shot out like a cork from a bottle. 'Peter Fenby.'

Jeremy burst out laughing. 'Peter Fenby? He's ten years younger than you. And he's just got married. What are you talking about?'

Marion continued down the road to disaster. Jeremy's infidelity, which she had taken at the time so calmly, became a weapon. 'You had a mistress. Why shouldn't I have a lover?'

That she had known about Janet, and said nothing, was a shock. That she had, as he saw it, said nothing about it, but revenged herself in this way raised such a wave of anger that he had to walk away for fear of actually hitting her.

The little chiming clock on the mantelpiece struck six. Marion heard it, and said, 'I'll go and do something about dinner.'

Jeremy had been intending to try and prepare something appetising for her. 'Don't bother,' he now said.

'But you must be hungry.'

'I'm not. I'm not in the least hungry.' Without another word, he left the house.

The problem was that there was nowhere to go. In London there was the office, with all its brash and worldwide money-making. There were clubs, streets, shops, women like Janet with those chic apartments which were really glorified whore-houses; hundreds of outlets where a man need think of nothing except his own requirements.

Here in Swanmere there was the Beaters' Arms. You didn't go down to the Beaters' Arms when your wife had just smashed your world into smithereens. And he could hardly drop in on the Fenbys!

For a while, Jeremy wandered. He crossed the village

green, where the swans swam dispassionately across the pond. Without knowing that he was following the tracks Peter had made, last September, he pushed his way through the little lane that led to the bottom of Marion's garden. And there? There, in its wildness, he wondered about Marion.

He had never considered in any depth the extraordinary contrast between this place of hers and her immaculate housekeeping. If he thought about it at all, it was as a place where she allowed the Fenby children to play, so they could racket about without messing up the house. She had always been kind to the Fenby children, presumably as a substitute for children of her own. Kind to the Fenby children, indeed! he thought bitterly.

He forced himself to recognise Peter Fenby as a man, as a cuckolder and, worst of all, as having done what he had been unable to do, which was to get his wife with child. 'That weed,' he said aloud. 'How could she?' Jeremy could only see Peter as bespectacled, unathletic, and not very successful at business. A man like Jeremy could never understand that Peter, to different eyes from his, could be very attractive. He, Jeremy, had taken the lead with Marion from the time he had comforted her when she was a frightened little girl with a dead mother. He, ever the big boy, had taught her all about sex. That she could turn to any other man was a blow; that it should be Peter was intolerable. He clenched his fists. Quite simply, he wanted to break Peter's neck. 'It's thin enough, it would break easily,' he muttered.

Striding about, he bumped into the old swing, seized and broke the ropes. In his rage, he then broke a branch of the cherry tree.

After Jeremy walked out, Marion went into the kitchen, got out the Flash and a new J-Cloth, and scoured the sink.

For months, she had not thought of Peter. Now, she remembered the sweetness of his kisses, the hollow below his graceful neck which she had so often kissed. She remembered his slim body, so light upon hers. She remembered the butterfly touch of his long, slim fingers, exploring so ardently but so courteously. Having Peter as a lover had been a charming experience. But she had rejected him, depriving him, without a qualm, of the baby he had given her.

At last, she wondered why she had done that. Why had she tricked Jeremy into believing the baby was his? Of course it was because she wanted her baby, and it had become *her* baby, and it was to have everything Jeremy could give it.

She went back into the drawing room. 'That sofa is new. So is the carpet,' she said. It was not the expense she thought about. It was that Jeremy had thought of and bought those things for her, while she was so ill in the hospital.

She opened the french windows and walked out on to the patio. This year, Jeremy had put standard roses into the big urns. She passed the barbecue, crossed the lawn, and went down into the wilderness.

She found Jeremy sitting on the ground, licking a cut on his hand. She sat down beside him, saying nothing. He did not touch her. She did not touch him. They just sat there, quietly.

'Poor Mrs Clark,' said Mrs Bean to Laura. 'But she's getting better, so that's something. And he's lovely to her. The new couch, new carpet, everything. Sad, though. My Sheila's ever so sorry for her. They're taking her in, next week. Going to induce the baby. Marvellous, what they can do, isn't it?'

'Sad about Marion Clark's baby, isn't it?' said Deirdre. She was now thinking that somewhere in Surrey might be a good idea. Much better than Swanmere. Not cheap, but worth it when you considered the swimming pools people had put in, in the eighties, when money was no object. Peter could be into Charing Cross in twenty minutes and everyone's children, in Surrey, went to private schools.

'Very sad,' said Peter guardedly. He supposed that, as the years went by, he would see Marion again. There would be

151

family gatherings, Easters, Christmases. But never again would he have the love he had had. Never again the garden, never again the run-aways, the secrets in nameless roadside rooms. Never again the champagne in the shower, never again the crisps and ginger beer in the bed. Never again the apricot breasts of Marion. Never again her taut, childless little body. Never again, never again.

'Mary,' said Luke, 'I think I might go round the world. What do you think about coming with me?'

'Back-packing? I don't think so.'

'You are rotten. It would be a lot more fun if you would come along.'

'No, it would not. It would be a total fucking nightmare. I have no intention of walking all over India and pretending it's an experience. The experience I prefer is first-class travel. You would have a very cross me, if I was silly enough to go along with you. But don't let me stop you. If you should wind up in New York, I might fly out and join you for a week.'

'Will you marry me one day?'

'I shouldn't think so. If I ever marry again, it'll be to someone rich and successful, not a poverty-stricken layabout like you.'

'He won't make you happy.'

'Yes, he will. I'll take good care of myself and stay pretty and look up at him admiringly in public. And he'll have mistresses, nice and safe because he's got a wife, and I'll have lovers. You, I hope.'

'You're awful.'

'So are you, sweetheart. I wouldn't marry you in a fit. Even the thought of your lovely mum as a mother-in-law wouldn't tempt me.'

It would be a long convalescence for Marion and Jeremy Clark. How they emerged together is private: no one's business but theirs.

21

'Daddy,' said Ann, 'I'm worried about Mummy.'

John Fenby had just come in from the garden, where he had seen Laura being bossed about by Len, in the patch where she grew her herbs. For his part, he thought she did very well with her mint, thyme, sage, rosemary and tarragon. He considered tarragon to be quite exotic enough, but nothing would do his son-in-law but the planting of many more fancy weeds. 'She's out doing some gardening,' he said.

Ann loved her father. She also knew him very well. Everything, in Daddy's world, was in its place. Perhaps that was why he had accepted, so equably, the arrival of Granny to live in the household of which he was head. In any case, Ann was well aware that her presence didn't really affect him all that much. For all that he loved her mother, she was fully aware of her father's ability to avoid being put out. 'Daddy,' she now said, 'if Granny stays here much longer, I really think that Mummy will –' she was going to say 'have a nervous breakdown' but she knew the thought of Laura having a nervous breakdown would be quite unbelievable to her father, so she substituted 'become ill.'

'Oh dear. I know Granny's getting a bit frail. Do you think the work is too much for Mummy? Perhaps I should tell her to have Mrs Bean more often.'

To say 'Granny? Frail? Frail, my foot, she's a wicked, selfish old monster' would be equally unacceptable, as much the wrong thing as to talk of nervous breakdowns. She changed tack. 'Surely you don't like Mummy sleeping in the nursery?

I read an article where it said old people ought to go on making love, it's good for their circulation.'

Whether he was stung by the 'old' or shocked at the prospect of discussing his bedroom arrangements with his daughter, this didn't seem to have been a very good idea, either. All she got back was, 'Well, hrmph, goodness me, is that the time? I have a vestry meeting.'

Laura, these days, was denied even the relief of Veronica's frequent visits to Marion's house, and the outings Marion had provided. She had made the veto herself. 'My dear girl, there is no question of your traipsing around the countryside with my mother. You may not realise how ill you've been, but we were all desperately worried about you.' Marion, now stuffed with vitamins and iron pills, privately thought she was in a good deal better shape than Laura.

'It seems,' said Veronica, deprived of what she saw as her 'one little outing', 'to be taking Marion a long time to get about. She's giving in, if you ask me.' Laura didn't ask her. She had reached a point where just getting from one day to the next without screaming was the best she could do.

It was as though her mental immune system had broken down. Her normally sensible attitude to the lives of her grown-up children gave way to worrying. She worried about Judy because Judy wasn't married. And she worried about Peter because he was. Whenever he and Deirdre visited, she would spend the hour before their arrival trying to like Deirdre, only to fail in Deirdre's presence. She was deeply ashamed of this antipathy, especially since Veronica came nearer to contentment when she had the companionship of her granddaughter-in-law. With Deirdre, she got a hearing for her complaints about Marion's self-indulgence. 'I haven't seen Marion for weeks. Of course, she has been ill, I know. But she just doesn't seem to try and make an effort.'

This was meat and drink to Deirdre, who had always envied Marion's lovely home and easy, spoilt existence. She also had a shrewd suspicion that Peter rather admired her. 'If Peter and I could only find a decent house,' she said, 'you could come and visit us. I'd love to have you, you're such an easy person to get along with.'

'Laura doesn't seem to think so. She never even seems to have time to talk to me. I don't know what keeps her so busy. But then, she never could organise herself.'

Deirdre very wisely steered away from this dangerous ground. Even she could see that ganging up against Peter's mother might backfire.

'Would you like it if I stayed on for a day or two?' she now asked. 'Peter has to go back on Sunday night, of course. But he can perfectly well catch the train, and leave me the car. And you and I could go somewhere.'

Laura was not consulted. But she had never been inclined to take an 'I am mistress of this house' attitude, which was just as well for Veronica, who would long have been got rid of by a daughter made of sterner stuff. In any case, the homoeopathic benefit was obvious, as Veronica and Deirdre set out together on Monday morning.

An outing with Deirdre turned out to be very much to Veronica's taste, for Deirdre was a keen shopper. Where Marion had always taken her to 'places of interest', Deirdre made like a homing pigeon for the nearest town with good shops, particularly in the dress line.

'Don't be silly, dear,' said Veronica, allowing herself to be persuaded to try on a dress. 'I'd have nowhere to wear it. I never go anywhere, these days. And if Laura entertains, though you can hardly call kitchen supper entertaining, an apron's more suitable for me than a silk dress.' Deirdre persuaded, Veronica refused.

It was time to have lunch, and once again their interests coincided at a chintzy establishment where Deirdre could eat salad while Veronica, on the grounds that it would save Laura trouble later, ate a large plate of fried fish and 'thin-cut golden potatoes', followed by lemon meringue pie. That Laura would be already preparing dinner conveniently escaped her calculations.

Deirdre would rather have liked to continue shopping after lunch; she hadn't had a chance to try on anything, herself. 'Would you like to pop back and have another look at that dress?' she asked.

Veronica was by now a very tired old woman who had just eaten more than was good for her. 'I don't think we should. It's been a long drive for you, you must be getting tired. We'd better make tracks.'

All that Deirdre had to look forward to was a long, dull evening with her in-laws. She paid for lunch with her married-lady credit card, escorted Veronica to the Ladies', and set off on a roundabout drive back to Swanmere.

A few miles outside the village, Veronica woke up from not being asleep and said, 'What's that? I don't remember seeing that house before.' The house was fronted by an immaculate lawn. A circular drive led in from the wrought-iron gates to a pillared entrance. 'There's a sign up. I wonder if it is for sale. Wouldn't it be lovely for you and Peter?'

The sign was not a For Sale sign. What it said, in elegant but noticeable lettering was, 'CATHAY MANOR. Exclusive Residence For Senior Gentlefolk. Inspection Invited.'

'Shall we take a quick look?' asked Deirdre, thinking simply of filling up another half-hour. 'I'm always interested in architecture, aren't you?'

This thinly veiled Old Folks' Home was short of punters. Veronica, in Deirdre's large car, was walking manna. The proprietor, dressed in tweeds to look like a golfing colonel, saw them through the window but did not rush to open the door. Once the bell had pealed twice (a proper jangle, no ding-dongs here) he approached ceremoniously. 'Good afternoon, ladies. May I help you?'

'We were just passing,' said Veronica, 'and we just thought, how charming.'

'How very sweet of you. Please, do come in and let me show you round.'

'We don't want to waste your time,' said Deirdre.

'Not in the least. My wife and I are very proud of Cathay Manor. We have only a few residents, all people we love to share our home with. We were reluctant, at first. But then, let me be honest, you can't keep this sort of place up to our standards on nothing. So it's all worked out very well.' The wife in question was even now dragging the day's washing out of a machine that should have been replaced last year. But it was, indeed, a beautiful house.

'What a delightful hall,' said Veronica. 'You so seldom see these black and white flagstones nowadays. Her sight was good, but not quite good enough to notice that the *Country Lifes*, *Lady's* and *Tatlers*, spread appetisingly on a low table, were anything between one and three years old. But the flowers were newly cut. Rhododendrons and azaleas fairly rioted in the garden, and the proprietor had awarded the privilege of collecting and arranging them to dear old Miss Fawcett-Smythe. His flattery obscured, for Miss Fawcett-Smythe, the real fact that she had spent a long and dismal spinsterhood arranging flowers for her mother and the church.

'And this is our dining room.' His wife was a good polisher and the sideboard, table and butler's tray were worth her efforts. They had come with the bankrupt manor. The tour was concluded with a short visit to the reading room, in which the books were impeccable. Job lots of unopened Dickens, Scott and Thackeray.

'May I offer you some tea?' said the proprietor, as taps and shuffles announced the arrival of residents, crossing the hall.

'No, thank you so much,' said Veronica. 'We really must be off, and we've taken up quite enough of your time.' She was beginning to think of a change of shoes and a gin and tonic before dinner.

'It's been delightful. So good of you to look in on us,' said the proprietor, glad not to have to show the bedrooms. The chambermaid, who shared the skivvying with his wife, was apt to get behind, and sometimes the bedrooms were not as dainty as might have been wished.

Laura, who had had her first day to herself for a long time, guiltily put down her book and rushed to the kitchen, fearing the chicken casserole would have turned to mush. As she had forgotten to switch on the oven, it was raw. She turned the oven as high as it would go, and hoped for the best.

'This chicken thing is nice,' said John, over supper. It wasn't all that nice, but he made a point of saying it was. Ann, for all that he had stomped away from her hints, had worried him. Veronica picked at her plate. Well, he thought, having dished her out two large pre-prandial drinks, if she doesn't like it, she can do without. He was glad to see a little colour in Laura's cheeks. Her hair looked nice, too. For once, Laura had had long enough privacy to wash it and let it dry slowly, the way that suited it, a wicked self-indulgence that had resulted in chicken with a burnt outside and a raw inside.

'Did you have a nice day?' Laura asked.

'We had a lovely day,' said Deirdre. 'We saw a dress I wanted Veronica to buy, but she wouldn't. Such a shame, it suited her marvellously.'

John got out a bottle of wine. It was not his best wine, but he hoped it would send Veronica to sleep. He wanted to make love to his wife. Too late, he remembered that they didn't sleep in the same room any more.

22

The proprietor of Cathay Manor, while he would not really have dreamed of dishonestly attempting to pass himself off as a retired colonel, had fallen into the way of referring, genially, to himself as Ted Matlock, thus avoiding the ordinariness of Mister.

He did not have a brochure, which not only saved money but also avoided the question of titles or qualifications, of which he had neither. Not that he was a villain. In fact Cathay Manor, with bluff Ted in charge, and not-so-bluff Mrs Ted doing most of the work, was actually a pleasant, rule-less place in which elderly persons with sufficient means could comfortably while away their declining years. Since even he was unable to swing a spirit licence in an old folks' home, he overcame the deficiency by being an obliging shopper for his residents' requirements. Two trips a year to France paid handsome dividends, and kept them far too happy to notice other small shortcomings.

Before he let Veronica and Deirdre go, Ted Matlock had subtly found out all he needed to know about Mrs Chadwick, and where she lived. Prime information was that she lived in her daughter's house, and had done so for far too long. It was also helpful that Theodor Carew came over, at least once a month, to give communion to old Miss Fawcett-Smythe and one or two others.

When Theodor Carew came to see her, Laura, at first, could not believe what she was hearing. She had reckoned without Theo Carew's unusual ability to do good in a mysterious way, and also his tact. For, although Theo had said to his wife Dorothy, 'Have you seen Laura Fenby lately? She looks absolutely worn out,' he had refrained from saying any such thing to Laura. All he said was, 'I've just dropped in on my way back from Cathay Manor.' Laura looked blank. He added, apparently inconsequentially, 'I really enjoy going there. I take communion to those who want it. I must say, if anyone I knew had to be taken good care of in old age, I'd be more than happy to see them there.'

Whether it was Miss Fawcett-Smythe's flower arrangements or the dining-room furniture, the thought of Cathay Manor had fixed itself attractively in Veronica's mind. Kitchen suppers, ironing never done from one week to the next, dust untouched unless it was Mrs Bean's day, Laura's longer and longer silences, no more visits to Marion Clark's house, all conspired to make the Grange less appealing by the day. In fact, the only thing the Grange had going for its self-invited occupant was that it was free. One did not deplete one's capital by paying to live with one's daughter.

But she kept remembering the dress she hadn't bought, the day she went shopping with Deirdre. It would look well on her at the Cathay Manor dinner table. And there had been rather a nice suit, pink tweed, which would look well at luncheon time.

Laura spent her days not snapping at her mother. She spoke pleasantly, while her gastric juices churned. A quick five minutes in the garden helped. But the day came.

It was a rainy, cold day; the sort of day that, in wintertime, with the central heating going, means crumpets for tea, lights switched on early, and doing the crossword puzzle by the fire; but in summertime, just plain dismal.

John had a summer cold but wouldn't go to bed. He might allow himself to take to his bed for a dose of flu in winter, but summer colds were to be ignored. He ignored his by sneezing all over the house, using up all the handkerchiefs that had, at last, been ironed, and wanting something to eat at least once every two hours.

Veronica was cold. But she, too, had her summer rules, and sat shivering over the *Daily Telegraph* in the drawing room, while John wandered in and out of the kitchen. It was also Mrs Bean's day. Dear Mrs Bean was everywhere, even in the bathroom. Laura had nowhere to hide.

By five o'clock, unable to get out into the garden, Laura felt as though she was going mad. She had served coffee and biscuits, a ham sandwich for John, consommé for Mummy, tomato soup and a cheese sandwich for John, tea and cake for both of them, and now she was wondering only whether she could hope to serve supper reasonably early, and then escape.

Looking round for what on earth to provide, she came across a bottle with a little bit of wine left in it. It just about half filled a glass, which she was swallowing as Veronica came into the kitchen.

'A bit early for that, isn't it?' said Veronica.

'I expect it is,' said Laura.

'I hope you are not becoming an alcoholic.'

'I don't think half a glass of Chianti constitutes alcoholism,' said Laura, her voice rising.

'There's no need to snap at me. I'm only thinking of you.' Seating herself at the kitchen table, with elaborate weariness, Veronica changed tack. 'You're tired of me, aren't you?'

'Of course not. It's just this awful weather.'

'Maybe I ought to go. I've done my best to be a help. But now I just feel I'm in the way.' This was said in a tone designed to indicate that any sense of her mother's being in the way was clearly Laura's fault. She held up a hand to forbid another 'Of course not.' 'I had hoped,' she continued, 'to leave you everything I've got when I die.'

'I've never thought of such a thing,' said Laura, fighting a desperate weariness.

Veronica gave a sad smile and a shake of the poor old head that knew better. 'However, I could just manage to keep myself elsewhere, as long as I don't live too long. That place, Cathay Manor, I believe it's called.'

Judy Fenby hadn't been to see her mother and father for months on end. Her work and her cool, orderly flat on the Battersea side of Albert Bridge kept her fully occupied. She gave dinner parties once every month. Cold soup, lobster claws in a new sauce every time, glazed grapes, ice-creams so subtle as to taste of nothing at all, cheese board and six at table. There would be an Interesting Couple, usually a couple she had recently met. Sometimes there would be Peter and Deirdre. Deirdre liked meeting interesting couples. And sometimes, when she could pin them down, Luke and Mary. And always a man to match numbers with herself.

She had, on her list, one divorced husband, one gay, one intellectual with no apparent sexual predilections and a complete inability to explain what he was being intellectual about, and one randy-boots. The last only came once. He didn't like the food, and made the mistake of thinking that Judy wouldn't have let him touch her.

Laura was surprised, one Friday evening, to receive a telephone call from Judy, who said, 'Could I come down for the weekend?'

'How nice. Peter and Deirdre will be here. Do you want to bring anyone?'

'No, no one. Will it be all right if it's just me?' Laura's heart went out to the daughter she knew least well of all her children. 'Of course.'

Even as she spoke, Judy was regretting the commitment she had now made. Maybe she had just signed away the one weekend when something good would happen. Maybe, as her mother continued to talk, someone lovely was trying to get through to her. Someone to be alone with, someone worth chucking the work she always did on Saturdays under the sofa for. Someone who wasn't asking her to make up a party and match with another out-of-town bore.

'You've heard about Granny?' she now heard her mother say.

'How is Granny?' asked Judy.

'All right, I think. You know she's at Cathay Manor now?'

'What's Cathay Manor?'

'I'll tell you all about it when I see you. I'm glad you want to come home.'

'See you tomorrow, then,' said Judy.

Peter and Judy had always been the quiet ones of the family. However, finding themselves out walking after lunch – Deirdre had gone to lie down with a headache – they sought a topic. After a long silence, each said at the same time, 'What a surprise, Granny moving out.'

Judy then continued, 'How did it come about?'

'I think it was the Vicar, in the end. But actually, it was Deirdre who took her to Cathay Manor in the first place.'

'Good for Deirdre. Mummy would never have suggested such a thing. But as it's turned out, Granny must have wanted it. Mummy would never have asked her to go. And then, from what Mummy said to me, it also had something to do with Marion. I know Granny used to go to her two or three times a week, and then she got bored when Marion couldn't do it any more. You knew she'd been very ill?'

'I heard something about it.' Peter walked on in silence. They were out of the village by now, Peter subconsciously leading the way in the opposite direction from the Clarks' house. They had reached a field familiar to them both from their childhood, a shapely field where their mother had often taken them for picnics, and were walking up the sloping, narrow path at its side, which meant going in single file.

'It was so sad about their baby,' said Judy. Peter seemed not to hear. The path broadened, and she came up beside him. 'I'd like to have children.'

The change of subject suited Peter. 'Well, you will,' he said.

'I'd have to be married first. And I'm not sure if that's ever going to happen. I mean, I'd like to be married. But . . .'

'Has there been anyone? Anyone you'd marry?'

'Only once. And he didn't like me enough. I thought I was pregnant, once, and he would have married me. But then, when it turned out that I wasn't, I could see that he was glad. So that was the end of that.' Judy had just said more about herself than anyone had ever heard. 'We ought to turn back soon. Deirdre will be wondering where you've got to.'

Peter was overwhelmed with a misery that almost made him sick. How coolly Judy had said, 'So that was the end of that.' If only he had been able to be as ruthless as that man, whoever he was!

Judy sat down on the dry grass. 'What's the matter, Peter?' she asked.

'Nothing.'

'Rubbish. We've begun to talk. It's usually Ann and Luke who talk, not us. So talk to me. Something's the matter, isn't it? Is it about Deirdre?'

'Not entirely. Well, yes and no. But it's certainly not her fault.'

'That means you're not in love with her. So why did you marry her?' asked Judy, unconscious of using the crisp tone of voice in which she might have asked her Board of Directors why they thought it necessary to open an office in Nottingham.

It was a method that suited Peter. Gushing sympathy would have clammed him up. 'I was living with her. Well, you knew that. I'd never found a place of my own, because I couldn't be bothered to.' Judy waited for more, and got it. 'I'd never really known what I wanted, in the way of a job. But I've always liked juggling with numbers; I suppose I'm actually rather good at it. So I took what I was offered, and it paid well. Still does.'

'So,' said Judy. 'That's your job. Let's talk about that another time. Tell me about Deirdre.'

'Well, she put me up for a night, after an office party. And then I moved in. You've seen the flat.'

'Indeed I have. It's lovely, smarter than mine.' Judy's own flat was very smart indeed.

'That's due to Deirdre, entirely. She's got tremendous energy, she's a perfectionist. And she's been very good to me. Even if I offer to do some Hoovering, she won't let me.'

'A bit like Marion Clark?'

'No,' said Peter, sharply.

'Right. Well,' said Judy. 'But the point is, after all that, you are not in love with her. Are you in love with someone else?'

'Yes.'

Judy picked some daisies and began to make a chain of them. 'Then why don't you get a divorce? Sorry. I don't mean to be unkind to Deirdre. But, even though I'd like to be married, *I* couldn't live with someone who didn't love me. I don't know her that well, but I think she's quite tough. You should come clean with her, get a divorce, and marry the woman you love.'

'It's Marion Clark,' said Peter bleakly.

For a while they sat quietly on the grass where they had long ago eaten the squashy banana sandwiches their mother knew to be their favourite, and blown down their lemonade straws to make rude noises.

23

'Well I never,' said Luke to Mary. 'What do you think? Old Pete's quit his job and gone off to Venice.'

'Has Deirdre gone with him?'

'I don't think so. All I know is, I popped into the flat, and there he was, stuffing a few socks and things into a sausage-bag. He just said "Oh, hallo Luke. I'm just packing a few things. I've quit my job and I'm going to Venice." I'll say this for Pete, he doesn't bore you with too much detail.'

'If Deirdre's got any sense,' said Mary, 'she'll get after him as fast as she can.'

'So that's what you think, is it? Then why don't you change your mind, and come round the world with me?'

'Not likely! Not me. I told you, I'll meet you in New York.'

'Peter's gone to Venice,' said Ann to Len. 'Lovely,' said Len. 'I've always wanted to go to Venice. We'll go there, one day. Think of all those restaurants. And the Italians grow wonderful vegetables.'

Laura Fenby showed her husband a postcard. 'Typical Peter,' she said. 'A picture of St Mark's Square, where he most certainly isn't staying, and he says "Having a wonderful time, wish you were here."'

'He doesn't,' said John. 'He doesn't wish any of us were there. Will you make me a Welsh rabbit for lunch please? I want something sustaining; I'm going over to that Cathay

Manor place this afternoon, to see your mother.'

Peter got off the vaporetto at Landing 10. The only reason he got off at Landing 10 was that he could see little winding streets. Humping his bag, which wasn't very heavy, he found himself a cheap hotel.

It was the sort of place where the proprietor had long learned to put up with orders of one plate of pasta between four people. It wouldn't have suited Deirdre. But then, Deirdre wasn't here.

Peter's sudden departure for Venice was a mystery to everyone. Everyone, that is, except Deirdre, because it was Deirdre's idea.

Deirdre had at last discovered the ideal house, in Swanmere, overlooking the village green. And because it needed renovation, it was for sale at a fairly reasonable price. 'Now,' she told Peter, 'all we have to do is to sell the flat. We can even come down a bit with the asking price. And we're sure to get a mortgage. It's a good thing your job is secure.'

They were in the flat. Peter had just come home from work, and had gone into the bedroom to take off his city suit. He looked in the mirror, and saw in it Deirdre's husband: suit immaculate, shirt well laundered, tie clean and carefully knotted. 'Secure,' he said aloud.

Deirdre had followed him into the bedroom. 'You don't seem to like the sound of the word,' she said. 'What's wrong with it?'

'Nothing. Only I'm not sure it applies to me. What would you say if I told you I'd been fired?'

'You haven't, have you?'

'No.' Suddenly, he knew it was now or never. 'No,' he said clearly. 'I haven't been fired. But I am going to resign.'

Deirdre swallowed. 'You mean, you're changing jobs?' she asked.

'No. I mean I'm quitting my job. I'm sorry Deirdre, but I can't go on.'

'What's that supposed to mean? Do you mean you can't go on with our marriage? Is there someone else?' This question of Deirdre's was hardly serious. Having someone else was simply something Peter wouldn't do. She knew him quite well enough to be sure of that. His sexual reluctance had never much worried her. She was one of those women for whom attracting men is an essential way of life. But making love was not important to her. She simply thought, if she thought about it at all, that Peter sometimes felt like sex, but quite often didn't.

She had married him because, in the first place, she did not want to remain single, a state to be dreaded. In the second place, she felt herself fortunate to have married, in the end, much better than had her younger sisters. Peter was a gentleman in every way, and she was proud of him.

According to her own set of rules, she had, she believed, filled her side of the bargain. She took trouble to make him comfortable, in what she thought of as being every way. In return, it was hardly unreasonable that she should expect to be a company wife. And now, he had dealt her a cruel blow.

She spoke very carefully. 'Let me understand this, Peter. You are resigning, without anything else in mind. You do realise that I gave up my job when we got married?' Peter remained silent. He was in no position to remind her that giving up her job was not a suggestion that had come from him. 'What?' asked Deirdre, 'do you suppose we are going to live on?'

'Deirdre, I don't know. I wanted to tell you, even before we were married, how much I hated my job. But I couldn't. Your mother had given you the lace tablecloth, and your father was dying. And in Venice, on our honeymoon, I didn't seem to find the chance.'

So, thought Deirdre in her usual language, I have been living in a fool's paradise. She wasted no time on recriminations. She never wasted either time or energy on losing her temper. She simply, now, reworked her plans. She was called Mrs. She had got that much out of it. But, as far as her own future was concerned, she would have to regroup, go on a diet, get her hair restyled, and start all over again. And who can blame her? 'I think,' she said, 'it would be better for both of us if you left here. Why not go to Venice?'

'It seems quite strange, just the two of us in the house,' said Laura, sitting up beside her husband in bed. It was nine o'clock in the morning, and the bed was a comfortable muddle of newspapers, letters and toast crumbs. John was opening the post; she always let him, as he complained that she tore while he neatly slit. On this occasion he happened to have slit with a marmalady knife. He looked at her over the spectacles he wore cock-eyed and half-way down his nose. 'Best enjoy it while you can. Read this.' And he handed her the sticky letter.

Dear Mum and Dad,
    We thought we'd write instead of ringing, because this is important. Ann and me are expecting. It's only two months, but it's been confirmed. Another reason for writing is, we want to ask you a favour, and give you a chance to get out of it if you want to. It's this. Can Ann stay with you for a bit, after the baby's born? I'll be too busy working to look after her properly. I'm going to try and take on puddings until she gets back, as we don't want anybody else in the kitchen.
    Lot of love,
    Len and Ann

'Well,' said John. 'It's up to you, of course. But I would have thought you'd had enough of looking after people.'
    'I have, for the moment. But it's not for another seven months.'
    'Oh well, at least it'll be too young to rattle door-handles.'

★

At Cathay Manor, Veronica Chadwick was doing, between tea and dinner, a jigsaw puzzle. Miss Fawcett-Smythe leaned over and looked. 'That piece doesn't fit,' she said.

Veronica, in pink tweed to Miss Fawcett-Smythe's beige cardigan and useful go-with-everything skirt, said happily, 'Doesn't it? It will. It always does, in the end.'